OXFORD*Playscripts*

Thomas Hardy   *adapted by David Calcutt*

Tess *of the* d'Urbervilles

D1637885

Oxford University Press

OXFORD
UNIVERSITY PRESS

Great Clarendon Street, Oxford OX2 6DP

Oxford New York
Athens Auckland Bangkok Bogotá Buenos Aires Calcutta
Cape Town Chennai Dar es Salaam Delhi Florence Hong Kong Istanbul
Karachi Kuala Lumpur Madrid Melbourne Mexico City Mumbai
Nairobi Paris São Paulo Singapore Taipei Tokyo Toronto Warsaw
and associated companies in Berlin Ibadan

Oxford is a registered trade mark of Oxford University Press

This adaptation of *Tess of the D'Urbervilles* © David Calcutt 1998
Activity section © Fiona Edwards 1998

First published 1998

ISBN 0 19 831439 6

Original music was composed by Peter Godfrey. Music for the songs
and dance-tunes can be obtained from: Peter Godfrey, 14 Deer Park,
Gnosall, Stafford ST20 0HQ.

The Publisher would like to thank the following for permission to reproduce
photographs:
Philip Mould, Historical Portraits Ltd, London, Bridgeman Art Library,
London/New York: p 114; The Matkins Collection/Bridgeman Art Library,
London/New York: p 116; Donald Cooper Photostage: p 132; Sally and
Richard Greenhill Photo Library: p 127; The Kobal Collection: pp 123,
124, 129, 130, 131; London Weekend Television: pp 122, 128; The Royal
Academy of Arts: p 125; Tate Gallery, London: p 117; Topham
Picturepoint: p 133.

The artwork is by Robert Goldsmith
Cover artwork by Simon Fell

Printed and bound in Great Britain at Cambridge University Press

Contents

Characters

In order of their
appearance on stage:

Tess Durbeyfield	*a young village girl*
Chorus 1-9	*a group of people who tell the story and comment on the action*
Rachel **Sarah**	*village girls*
Angel Clare	*a clergyman's son, who rejects his upbringing in favour of modern ideas about life and work*
John Durbeyfield	*Tess's father*
Villager 1 **Villager 2** **Villager 3** **Villager 4**	*neighbours and acquaintances of the Durbeyfields*
Parson Tringham	*the local vicar, a rather superior man*
Joan Durbeyfield	*Tess's mother*
Abraham	*Tess's younger brother*
Liza-Lu	*Tess's younger sister*
Alec d'Urberville	*a wealthy, young landowner who takes a fancy to Tess*
Car Darch **Nancy Darch** **Lizzie Darch**	*women who work for Alec d'Urberville*
Mr Richard Crick	*chief dairyman at Talbothays Dairy*
Mrs Alice Crick	*his wife*
Jonathan Kail	*a dairyman at Talbothays*
Marion Hardy **Izz Huett** **Retty Priddle**	*dairymaids at Talbothays*

Reverend Clare	*Angel's father*
Mrs Clare	*Angel's mother*
Jack Dollop	*a milker who used to work at Talbothays, one for the girls*
Rebecca Brook	*a young girl deceived by Jack*
Mrs Brook	*Rebecca's formidable mother*
Man 1 **Man 2** }	*observers at Tess and Angel's wedding*
Landlady	*at a lodging house in Sandbourne*
	Act 1, Scene 1 requires a group of village girls who dance

Before You Read the Play

Before you read this play, you might find it useful to know what I had in mind when I wrote the script, and worked on its first performance. I adapted **Tess of the D'Urbervilles** for a particular production, and this is reflected in many ways throughout the text. These notes, of course, are given simply as a guide to show you how we did it. You may have your own quite different ideas on how it might be produced on stage.

Our production was designed to use a single, simple, all-purpose set, and to play end-on to the audience. It looked something like this:

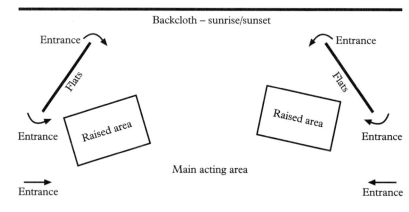

Backcloth – sunrise/sunset
Entrance
Entrance
Flats
Flats
Raised area
Raised area
Entrance
Entrance
Main acting area
Entrance
Entrance

To keep things simple and 'uncluttered' we used as few props as possible, and most of these were brought on and off by the actors. Anything left on-stage was removed, when appropriate, during a blackout. A number of props, however, did need to be placed on-stage at the beginning of an act. These were usually put out of sight, behind one of the raised areas of the set, until required.

- Act One: the cloak, bonnet and basket given to Tess by the Chorus as she leaves for her first journey to Trantridge.
- Act Two: the crown of flowers worn by Tess at her wedding, and the travelling bag picked up by Angel after the wedding.

Lighting was also kept to a minimum, and references in the script to any simple lighting changes are there as a guide.

You will see that the play is divided into scenes as well as acts. This was done with the classroom reader in mind, to provide convenient break points in the action. Our production, however, used no such breaks and the performance of each act was continuous and flowing.

Finally, we used two groups of Chorus, each consisting of nine actors. These two groups also took on the roles of some of the minor characters in the play. However, there are a number of ways of presenting the Chorus – from a single group of nine throughout, to a different group of nine for each act. You may come up with other variations to suit the needs of your production.

David Calcutt

Act 1
· · · · · · ·

Scene 1

The lights rise. **Tess** *enters, alone. She wears a simple, white dress. She kneels centre stage and sings.*

Tess

As I walked out one morning all in the month of May,
I saw a man all dressed in black upon the broad highway.
Black was his hair, blue were his eyes, and cold as cold could be,
'Oh, come away, my love,' he said, 'Oh, come away with me.'

Chorus 1 – 3 enter. They stand, one on each side of Tess, and one behind, to form a triangle around her. One of them carries a willow wand and gives it to Tess.

Chorus 1

This is how the story begins –

Chorus 2

This is where the story begins –

Chorus 3

In the village of Marlott, in the Vale of Blackmoor –

Chorus 1

Hidden among the high, rolling hills of Wessex –

Chorus 2

In the secret heart of that ancient kingdom –

Chorus 3

Of tales and ballads, and age-old songs.

Tess sings.

Tess

'Who are you, sir?' I said to him, 'I fear you do me wrong.'
'What is your name and country?
What place do you belong?'
'I am your own true lover, as true as true can be.
Come away with me and be my bride,' are the words he said to me.

Chorus 4 – 6 enter. They take up the same positions as Chorus 1 – 3. One of them carries a bunch of mayblossom, and gives it to Tess.

Chorus 4

And this is Tess. Tess Durbeyfield –

Chorus 5	Sitting here weaving a crown of flowers –
Chorus 6	The village and valley are her only world –
Chorus 4	The endless days, the turning seasons –
Chorus 5	Where she lives her life without shadow or shame –
Chorus 6	An innocent maid, a pure woman.

Tess sings.

Tess	Then he reached out and took my hand, and his touch was icy cold. And as he drew me to him, I felt the year turn old. The sky grew dark, the wind blew sharp, the leaves fell from the tree, 'Oh, come with me, my love,' he said, 'for all eternity.'

> *Chorus 7 – 9 enter. They take up the same positions as the other members of the Chorus. One of them carries a crown of flowers. It is placed on Tess's head. She stands.*

Chorus 7	It's Maytime, and the air is fine and clear –
Chorus 8	The sky blue, the valley warm under the sun –
Chorus 9	She stands, puts the crown of flowers in her hair –
Chorus 7	And with a willow wand in one hand, mayblossom in the other –
Chorus 8	Her white dress shining in the mid-morning light –
Chorus 9	She dances.

> *A fiddle takes up the melody of Tess's song, turning it into a lively tune. Village girls (including **Sarah** and **Rachel**) enter and dance. The **Chorus** move back in two groups to stand around and behind the two raised areas. They clap along with the music.*

*The fiddle is joined by other instruments – flute, drum, and so on, and the tempo increases. For a short time **Tess** watches, then **Sarah** and **Rachel** approach her, and she joins them in the dance.*
*__Angel__ enters. He stands to one side, watching. The dance ends. The dancers go, leaving only **Sarah**, **Rachel** and **Tess** together. They prepare themselves for the next dance, brushing down dresses, re-arranging hair, and so on. **Tess** takes off the crown of flowers and puts down the willow wand and the mayblossom. **Angel** turns and speaks to the audience. During his speech, the three girls become aware of his presence.*

Angel	And that was where I first saw her. I was spending the Whitsun holidays walking through the Blackmoor Vale, coming down from Shaston and making for Stourcastle. The sound of music drew me to the village green, and so I stopped to watch for a while. *(He turns to look at Tess)* There was nothing particularly remarkable about her. Her beauty and freshness were no more than those of the other village girls. But there was something about her… a look… an air of… vulnerability… that seemed to set her apart.

Sarah approaches Angel.

Sarah	Are you going to join us in our dancing, sir?
Angel	I think I might well do.
Rachel	Sarah! You shouldn't be so forward!
Sarah	I'm not! I'm only saying what he already has on his mind. That's right, isn't it, sir?
Angel	It is – but, there is only one of me.
Sarah	One man's better than no man at all, isn't it, Rachel? Now, sir. You must choose between us. Who'll be your partner?
Angel	It's not an easy choice –

Rachel	I'll make it for you, then!
	Rachel pushes past Sarah and takes hold of Angel. The music starts up and they dance. Tess watches Angel throughout the dance. It is obvious that she wants him to dance with her. After a short time, Sarah takes over from Rachel to dance with Angel. The dance continues with Sarah and Rachel alternately taking Angel as their partner, until it ends, with Rachel as the final partner.
Rachel	*(Indicating Tess)* And now you must dance with Tess. She won't ask you herself.
	Angel and Tess face each other.
Angel	The music's finished.
Rachel	Davey can soon strike up another.
	Angel approaches Tess.
Angel	No… I can't stay any longer.
Sarah	One more dance won't hurt.
	Angel is about to change his mind, but checks himself.
Angel	I'd like to… but I must be going… I'm sorry…
	Angel turns and moves away from Tess towards the side of the stage. He speaks to the audience.
Angel	So I left her, and went on along the lane, away from the village. But at the next rise, I stopped and looked back. And I could see her, a small figure standing alone in the afternoon sunlight. I wished then I had stayed. I wished I'd danced with her. Somehow I felt I'd… let her down. But it couldn't be helped, and I turned away, and by the time I reached the next bend I'd forgotten her. And even when I met her again, three years later, I didn't remember seeing her before, or who she was.

Angel goes. Tess moves a few steps after him, looking towards where he has gone.

Chorus 1   But if he had stayed –

Chorus 2   If he had stayed and danced with her –

Chorus 3   If he'd taken her hand and asked her name –

Chorus 4   Who knows what might have happened then?

Chorus 5   Who can tell what the story might have been?

Chorus 6   But there's only one story that we can live –

Chorus 7   Only one tale our lives can tell –

Chorus 8   The one fixed into us at our very beginning –

Chorus 9   And we must live it through to its bitter end.

John Durbeyfield enters, accompanied by four villagers. He is drunk and is waving a half-empty bottle in the air. The villagers are making merry at John's expense.

Villager 1   Make way! Make way for John Durbeyfield!

Villager 2   Bow your knees to my Lord John!

Villager 3   Lord John d'Urberville!

Villager 4   Make way for the royal Lord of Kingsbere!

Tess   Father… ?

John   I got a great family vault! I got knighted forefathers at Kingsbere!

Tess   What's going on?

Rachel   Looks like he's been down at Rollivers.

Sarah   And taken a bit too much for his own good.

Tess	That's enough! I won't have you talking about my father like that!
John	John d'Urberville, that's me! Lord John d'Urberville of Kingsbere!
Villager 1	Three cheers for Lord John!

> *They cheer as **John** throws back his head and drains the bottle. On the third cheer, he falls backwards. The **villagers** catch him and heave him, staggering back onto his feet.*

John	Tess! Daughter! We be of a noble race!
Tess	Be quiet, Father!
John	It's recorded in the history all about us.
Tess	I think I'd best take you home.
John	What's my name, Tess? Eh? Tell me! What's my name? Go on! Say it!
Tess	John Durbeyfield.
John	No! D'Urberville! That's who I am! John d'Urberville! And I've got a whole vault of ancestors to prove it. Hundreds of them, lying in great lead coffins, in coats of mail, and jewels –
Tess	This is just foolishness.
John	No, it's not! It has been found out to me this very afternoon!
Villager 1	It's true. Parson Tringham told him.

> *__Parson Tringham__ enters. He stands apart from the rest, to show that his scene with John is a flashback, narrated by the villagers. __John__ stands between the villagers and Parson Tringham, enabling him to turn repeatedly from the flashback conversation to the present one.*

Parson Tringham is an educated man, rather haughty, and a little amused by John, and the discovery he's made about him.

Villager 2   He was coming home from Shaston and he met the parson coming the other way –

Parson Tringham takes a step towards John.

Villager 3   And the parson says to him –

Parson Tringham   Good day to you, Sir John.

Villager 4   *(To Tess)* And your father, he stops, and he looks at the parson, and he says to him –

John   What was that you called me?

Parson Tringham   I called you Sir John.

John   And why might you call me that –

Villager 1   Says John –

John   – when I'm just plain Jack Durbeyfield, the haggler?

Parson Tringham   I don't mean to offend you, Lord John Durbeyfield –

John   *(Interrupting)* There you go again!

Parson Tringham   – but it's really only a whim.

John   A whim?

Villager 2   A whim –

Villager 3   That's what he said –

Villager 4   A whim.

John   And what's the meaning of this here whim?

Villager 1	Then the parson, he takes a step or two nearer to John, and he looks him up and down, and he says –
Parson Tringham	It is on account of a discovery I made some little time ago, when I was hunting up pedigrees for the new county history. Don't you know, John Durbeyfield, that you are the lineal representative of the ancient and knightly family of the d'Urbervilles, who derive their descent from Sir Pagan d'Urberville, that renowned knight who came from Normandy with William the Conqueror, as appears in the Battle Abbey Roll?
Villager 2	And Jack Durbeyfield –
Villager 3	Sir Jack Durbeyfield –
Villager 4	He looks back at the parson and he says –
John	What's all that mean, then?
Parson Tringham	What it means, John Durbeyfield, is this.
Villager 1	And Parson Tringham steps in closer, and he says to John –
Parson Tringham	You are the last living descendant of a once great and noble family –
Villager 2	– the d'Urbervilles –
Parson Tringham	– who once held land and manors all over this part of England –
Villager 3	– who fought in wars and served with kings –
Parson Tringham	– and were at one time wealthy and powerful beyond compare. And that if knighthood were hereditary –
Villager 4	– which it isn't –
Parson Tringham	– you'd be Sir John, now.

John turns out of the flashback, and back to the villagers.

John	That's what he said! That's just what Parson Tringham says to me. True as I'm standing here. I got noble ancestors, going back beyond Oliver Grumble's time – back to the pagan Turks – and they're all lying in the city of Kingsbere.
Villager 1	City, did you say, John? The *city* of Kingsbere?
John	That's right.
Villager 1	I've been to Kingsbere, and it's no city. A little one-eyed, blinking sort of place, it is.

John grows angry. He swings out at the villagers with his bottle, staggering among them.

John	It don't matter what the place is! It's where they lie – my ancestors – under the church – rows and rows of them – there ain't a man got grander nor nobler skellintons in all Wessex.

He swings again wildly with his bottle, stumbles, and falls. **Tess** *runs to him.*

Parson Tringham	*(To the audience, with some irony)* Not that it will do him any good to know it. There's nothing left of them. Gone down, and gone under. Nothing left but their tombs and their bones. *(To John, amused)* Good afternoon, Sir John.

Parson Tringham goes.

Tess	Father. Are you all right? Have you hurt yourself?
Villager 2	How are the mighty fallen. And fallen mighty low, as well.
Villager 3	Arise, Sir John. If you can.
John	I'll rise! I'll rise again, you see if I don't.

John tries to get up. He falls back.

Villager 4	*(To Tess)* I think you'd best take your noble father home. And lay him to rest in his family vault.

The villagers, Rachel and Sarah go, laughing. John calls out.

John	You can laugh – I'm as good as some folks here – and better than most.

Tess helps her father to his feet.

Tess	All right, Father! Quiet, now. That's enough of this nonsense.
John	It's not nonsense, Tess. It's true. All of it's true – great folks we've been – and will be again.
Tess	All right. I believe you… now, we'd best get you home.
John	That's right. Let's get home and tell your mother, and we'll see what she has to say about it.

Joan Durbeyfield enters and approaches John and Tess.

Joan	(*To John and Tess*) What do I have to say about it? I'll tell you what I have to say about it. We'll be fools if we don't make something of this, that's what we'll be.

Abraham and Liza-Lu enter, excitedly.

Abraham	We've got ancestors in grand tombs!
Liza-Lu	Our forefolk were all ladies and gentlemen!
Abraham	We're going to be ladies and gentlemen, aren't we, Tess?
Tess	I don't know.
Joan	Abraham. Liza-Lu. Help your father to his bed. He's had a trying day and it's worn him out.

The two children help their father off-stage.

Liza-Lu	Is it true, Father?
Abraham	Are we gentlefolk?

John	We are – with vaults and crests and 'scutcheons.
Abraham	What's a 'scutcheon?
John	Don't you know that? It's what all royal gentlefolk have.

They exit.

Tess	*(To Joan)* I haven't seen him like that for a long time. When he came along like he did this afternoon, with everybody there, I could've sunk into the ground with shame.
Joan	There's nothing to be ashamed of in your father, Tess. 'Specially now, knowing what kind of blood runs in his veins. And yours too.
Tess	There's no meaning to any of that.
Joan	Don't you be so sure. When word of this travels around, it wouldn't surprise me if people didn't come calling on us from all over.
Tess	What people?
Joan	Gentlefolk. Our kin.
Tess	But the parson said Father was the last of the line.
Joan	The last of the line direct. But there may be others. Sure to be. Cousins and whatnot. They'll be turning up here, in their carriages and finery –
Tess	No, they won't.
Joan	They will! You'll see! We haven't heard the last of this. Not if there's any justice in the world. It's time we had a turn for the better. God knows we've had enough for the worse. You think on it, Tess. Something will come of it all. I'll make certain it does.

Tess and Joan turn to face the audience for the narrative spoken by the Chorus.

Chorus 1	And something comes of it, sure enough –

Chorus 2	Because if John Durbeyfield hadn't heard that news from Parson Tringham –
Chorus 3	And if he hadn't gone and got himself drunk on account of it –
Chorus 4	Then he'd have been fit to drive the horse and cart to market next morning.

John enters and speaks to the audience.

John	*(Bitterly)* But I wasn't so I didn't, and Tess drove it instead.
Tess	A long journey, through narrow lanes, in the dark of the early morning.
Chorus 5	And if Tess hadn't been so tired that she fell asleep as she was driving –
Chorus 6	Then the accident would never have happened.

Joan looks sharply at Tess.

Joan	Accident? What accident?
Tess	*(Turning to Joan in distress)* Prince is dead, Mother. I'm sorry...
John	Dead? How did it happen?
Chorus 7	She was woken from her sleep by a sudden jolt.
Chorus 8	Ahead of her in the dark, she saw the morning mailcart –
Chorus 9	– with its shaft driven into the horse's chest.
Tess	*(Turning back to audience)* I tried to do something... I jumped down from the cart... and he was standing there, breathing slow and heavy... and with that big wound in his chest... I put my hands over it... I tried to stop the blood... but it just kept coming... *(She stares down at her hands in horror)*... all over my hands... all that blood.

Abraham enters.

Abraham	*(To Joan)* It's because we live on a blighted star.

Joan	What's that?
Abraham	Tess said. She told me we lived on a blighted star.

> ***Abraham*** *runs to Tess and cries.* ***Tess*** *hugs him.*

John	*(To Abraham)* Don't say such things. *(To Tess)* And you mustn't blame yourself.
Tess	But what will we live on, now? It's all my doing. To think I was laughing and dancing only yesterday. To think I was such a fool.
John	Things happen as they must. It's done, and there's nothing you can do to help it.
Joan	I wouldn't be so sure. There's never anything so bad happens it can't be turned to some good. And never could your high blood have been found out at a more called-for moment.
John	Do you have something in mind?
Joan	I have. It's a project I've been thinking of.
John	What project?
Joan	To set Tess on the road to becoming a lady.
Tess	What? What's all this about, Mother?
Joan	I've heard there's a lady lives out by Trantridge, at the edge of The Chase. She's rich, and she has the name of d'Urberville.
John	That's our name. Are you sure?
Joan	I'm certain of it. D'Urberville's her name, which means she must be a relation of ours. And with this trouble that's come upon us, I think that Tess must go to her and claim kin.
Abraham	*(Happy again)* Tess is going to claim kin with a lady! Tess is going to become a lady!

He runs off, excitedly.

Tess
I don't think I care to do this, Mother.

Joan
You don't care to? Why not?

Tess
It isn't right to go begging.

Joan
It's not begging. It's natural for families to ask help of each other in times of trouble.

Tess
We don't know that she is our family.

Joan
Her name's d'Urberville, isn't it? And hasn't your father been told that's his name as well? We must be related, and you must go and ask her for help. With your looks and your nature you'll win her round to anything.

Tess
I'd rather find some other way. I'll get work –

*In frustration, **Joan** turns to her husband.*

Joan
Durbeyfield! You must settle this! You're her father. If you say she ought to go, she will.

John
Well now. I don't know that I like my children going and making themselves beholden to strange kin –

***Joan** gives him a warning glance.*

John
– but I'm the head of the noblest branch of the family, and I ought to live up to it. It won't do no harm to go and see her, Tess.

Joan
There. Now it's settled.

***Tess** looks at her parents, hesitates, then makes up her mind.*

Tess
Very well. It was me killed the horse, and I ought to do something. I will go and see her, and introduce myself. And if I decide to ask her for help, that's my business. But that's all there'll be to it, and nothing more.

Tess turns from her mother and father, and approaches the Chorus. In turn, Chorus members hand her a cloak, a bonnet, and a basket. She takes them and goes. As this happens, Joan and John speak to each other.

Joan	There, now. We've set her on her way, and there'll be no going back. This is only the start of it. She's sure to win the lady, and to be taken into her house. And after that, well, one thing will lead to another.
John	What do you mean?
Joan	It won't be long before some gentleman sees her, and takes a fancy to her.
John	So that's your scheme. I don't know that Tess will have anything to do with something like that. You know what she's like.
Joan	Just you leave her to me, John Durbeyfield. This is a fine chance providence has brought her way, and it's our duty to do all we can to help her to it.

Joan and John exit. The Chorus leave, individually, on their lines.

Chorus 1	So she goes on her way, early next morning –
Chorus 2	Walking to the hill-town of Shaston –
Chorus 3	And taking the van that travels from there to Chaseborough –
Chorus 4	And passes by way of Trantridge –
Chorus 5	And there she gets out and walks again towards The Chase –
Chorus 6	Which is one of the last remaining ancient woodlands of England –
Chorus 7	And comes at last in sight of the great, red-brick country house –
Chorus 8	Newly-built in a landscape of lawns and gardens –

Chorus 9	Her destination, the home of the d'Urbervilles.

The stage is empty.

Scene 2

*Alec enters. He speaks to the audience, gradually making his way up onto one of the raised areas. About halfway through his speech, **Tess** enters, opposite. She is wearing her cloak and bonnet and is carrying a basket. She makes her way towards Alec.*

Alec	The irony is, of course, that we aren't d'Urbervilles at all. Stoke was my father's name, God rest his soul, and he made his money in the north. How he made it, we won't go into now. But, having made it, the old man decided he wanted to settle in the south, set himself up as a country gentleman. The simple name Stoke wouldn't do for that, of course. Far too plain and... business-like. So he did a little research, dug up the name of an old extinct family from the area, and... bought it. So, Simon Stoke became Simon Stoke d'Urberville. And having become that, he passed on, and left me, as his only son and heir, house, estate, property – and name. Not that she's aware of this, of course. And I'm pleased to say she isn't. Otherwise, she would never have come here, and I wouldn't have met such an enchanting creature.

Tess stands at the foot of the raised area and speaks to Alec.

Tess   Excuse me, sir…

Alec   Yes? What can I do for you?

Tess   I… I've called to see Mrs d'Urberville.

Alec   I'm afraid you can't. Mrs d'Urberville is not well. She's an invalid.

Tess   Oh…

Alec   Perhaps I can be of help. I'm her son. What is it you wanted to see her about?

Tess   It's difficult…

Alec   Business? Or pleasure.

Tess   I can't really say… perhaps I'd just better go.

Tess turns to go.

Alec   No – stay. As you've taken all the trouble to come out here, you may as well tell me why. Now. Try again.

Tess hesitates, then turns back, determined, and steps up towards him.

Tess   It was Mother asked me to come… to introduce myself… we're of the same family as you –

Alec   Ah. Poor relations.

Tess   Yes, sir.

Alec   Stokes?

Tess   No, sir. D'Urbervilles.

Alec   Yes, of course. D'Urbervilles.

Tess	Our name's worn away to Durbeyfield – but we have proofs that we are d'Urbervilles –
Alec	I'm sure you do.
Tess	– and our horse has been killed and Mother said I should call on you on account of us being the oldest branch of the family.
Alec	Are you, indeed? I see. So, you've come on a… friendly visit to us?
Tess	I suppose I have, yes.
Alec	Then we ought to introduce ourselves. My name's Alec.
Tess	I'm Tess.
Alec	Tess d'Urberville.
Tess	Durbeyfield, sir.
Alec	Of course. Tess Durbeyfield. And where are you from, Tess?
Tess	Down Marlott way, sir.
Alec	Alec, please.
Tess	From Marlott… Mr d'Urberville.
Alec	I'm delighted to meet you, Tess Durbeyfield from Marlott.

Alec holds out his hand. *Tess* takes it. He does not let go.

Alec	You said you'd lost your horse.
Tess	Yes. He was killed in an accident, and he was our only means of livelihood. And it was my fault; I feel I must do something to make amends for it.
Alec	And so you've come to see us.
Tess	Yes.

Alec	To ask for help.
Tess	*(Proudly)* Yes.
Alec	You're very bold. I admire that. I'll have a word with my mother, and see if she can find a position for you here. I make no promises, mind. But I'll do what I can.
Tess	Thank you, sir.
Alec	Alec. I insist. We are cousins.
Tess	Alec.
Alec	Good.

He lets go of her hand.

Tess	I'll be on my way, then.
Alec	Yes.
Tess	Goodbye.
Alec	I trust it's not.
Tess	Sir?
Alec	I hope we shall be meeting again before long – cousin.
Tess	Yes...

> *Tess turns, steps down from the raised area, moves away, and takes up a position at the back of the stage, turned away from the audience. Alec watches her go.*

Alec	Yes, my beauty, I do hope so indeed. *(He turns back to the audience)* But nothing is moved by hope alone. So, to that end, even as she's still within sight, I write a quick letter to her mother and father –

> *Alec takes out a small notepad and pencil and writes.*

Alec	– signed Mrs d'Urberville –
	Alec tears off a sheet, folds it, and puts the notepad and pencil away.
Alec	– get on my horse, ride down to Marlott, find the Durbeyfield residence –
	*Alec steps down from the raised area as **Joan** and **John** enter. He turns and speaks to them.*
Alec	Alec d'Urberville. Pleased to make your acquaintance.
Joan	*(To Alec)* The pleasure's ours, sir.
Alec	*(To audience)* – deliver the letter –
	*Alec hands the letter to **John**, who unfolds and reads it.*
John	*(To Joan)* It's from Mrs d'Urberville!
Alec	*(To audience)* – and it's done, and I'm gone –
John	*(To Alec)* Thank you, sir.
Joan	And thank your mother as well.
	Alec nods to Joan and John, then turns back to the audience.
Alec	– and all before Tess has got back home.
	*Alec goes. **Tess** approaches Joan and John.*
Joan	Tess! I said you'd do it! I knew you'd win her round.
Tess	What do you mean?
	John holds up the letter.
John	We've had a letter. From Mrs d'Urberville.
Tess	What?

Joan	She wants you to go and live there, Tess. There's a little fowl farm she has, and you're to look after it for her. That's right, isn't it, John?
John	*(Waving the letter)* It's just what it says here.
Joan	But that's not the true meaning of it. It's only a way of bringing you there so she can claim you for her kin and take you into her family.
John	She must have taken a liking to you, Tess.
Tess	But I didn't see Mrs d'Urberville.
Joan	You must've seen somebody.
Tess	Yes. Her son –
John	It was her son brought the letter.
Tess	He did say he'd speak to his mother.
Joan	And he has, and this is what's come of it. You've made more than a fair impression on him, Tess. And that's even better. A mighty handsome man, he is –
Tess	Mother!
Joan	And you so good-looking yourself, and being his cousin, it wouldn't surprise me if before long –
Tess	No! That's enough of that!

*Liza-Lu and **Abraham** enter.*

Liza-Lu	Tess! Mother says you're going to live at a grand house.
Abraham	And marry a gentleman and become a lady.
Liza-Lu	And we'll come and visit you and wear fine clothes.
Abraham	And we'll all be ladies and gentlemen.
Tess	*(To her mother)* What have you been telling them?

Joan	Nothing. Only that you're going to live up at Trantridge.
Tess	Well, I'm not. It's kind of her to offer me a place... but I've decided. I won't be going.
Liza-Lu	Why not, Tess? You must go.
Abraham	We want you to be a lady.
Liza-Lu	Why won't you go?
Tess	Because... somehow I feel nothing good will come of it.
Joan	You couldn't be more wrong, girl. Nothing but good can come of it!
Tess	I'd rather stay here and find other work.
Joan	Tess, you're a fool. This is your chance. Look about you. Look at how we live. Haven't you always wanted more than this?
Tess	Yes...
Joan	Then now's your chance! Once you're placed there –
Tess	I don't think it would turn out as you're thinking, Mother.
Joan	The girl's driving me to distraction! John. Will you make her see sense?
John	I'm not so sure about it myself.
Joan	What!
John	I don't know as I like the thought of Tess going away from home.
Joan	But she has to! *(She turns to Tess)* You owe it to yourself. It isn't often such an opportunity comes to one of our station, and when it does, it's a crime and sin not to take it. You're a lady in blood, and you must now go and claim what's yours by birthright.

Tess *turns to her father.*

Tess   Father – what should I do?

John   As I said – I don't like it. (*Joan gives John a shove from behind*) But your mother's right. It is a chance. You must go.

Joan   It's not just for yourself. It's for all of us.

Tess considers, then decides.

Tess   All right. I'll go.

John   It'll be for the best. Great things may come of it.

Joan   Great things will come of it. I know. I've seen it told in the stars.

Four villagers, Rachel and Sarah enter. They take up positions on either side of the stage, in two groups of three, gossiping across to each other. During their exchange, Joan, John, Abraham, and Liza-Lu fetch a best hat, gloves and a small travelling-bag. They take Tess's basket and help her change from her bonnet and cloak, in preparation for her journey.

Rachel   You hear about Tess Durbeyfield? She's going to live up at that big house at Trantridge.

Villager 1   We ain't good enough for her anymore. Going to mix with her new-found kin.

Villager 2   She's always thought herself a bit above the rest of us.

Villager 3   Not that she's had call to, with a slack-handed father like Jack Durbeyfield.

Villager 4   It's not Jack Durbeyfield no more. It's Lord John d'Urberville.

Villager 1   Them old names don't meaning nothing. There's plenty of families round here can trace themselves back to noble folk.

Sarah   It's all her mother's doing. I heard her saying how it's her plan for Tess to marry into the gentry.

Villager 2	And you know what comes of plans like that. She wants to mind Tess don't come back from Trantridge with more than she took with her.
Villager 3	And she won't be the first, nor the last.
Sarah	I've nothing against the girl. She's got a kind heart and makes a fine figure.
Rachel	I saw her walking out the other day. All in white. So fair, she looked.
Villager 4	Yes. Just like an innocent lamb on its way to the slaughter.

> *The **villagers, Sarah** and **Rachel** go. **Tess** is ready now. **Joan** holds her cloak, bonnet and basket.*

Joan	There, now. You're ready. And doesn't she look handsome?
John	She does. Like a real lady.
Joan	That's just what she is. And just what she'll be.
Tess	Goodbye, Father.
John	Goodbye, my love. See that you look after yourself.
Tess	I will.

> *John goes.*

Liza-Lu	Goodbye, Tess.
Tess	*(Hugging Liza-Lu)* Goodbye, Liza-Lu.
Abraham	*(Hugging Tess)* Won't we ever see you again?
Tess	Course you will, Abraham. I'll come and visit when I can.

> *Liza-Lu and Abraham go.*

Joan	Well. You'd best be on your way, now.

Tess	Yes. Goodbye, Mother.

> *Tess turns and begins to walk away. Joan suddenly calls out.*

Joan	Tess!

> *Tess turns back. It's as if Joan wants to tell her something she should have told her before, but realizes now that it's too late. So, she just says, simply.*

Joan	Take care.

> *Tess is about to reply when Alec enters and approaches her.*

Alec	There's no need for concern, Mrs Durbeyfield. Tess is in my care, now.

> *Joan goes. Alec speaks to Tess, drawing close to her.*

Alec	My charge. My keeping. My sweet maid.

> *Alec holds out his hand for Tess's bag. She hands it to him. He takes it, imprisoning her hand and the handle of the bag in his.*

Alec	A kiss, cousin.
Tess	Sir?
Alec	Let me have a kiss.
Tess	Why?
Alec	Why not? We're kinsfolk, aren't we?
Tess	Yes…
Alec	There's no harm in it, is there?
Tess	I don't know…

Alec	A single kiss, then.
Tess	*(Sharply)* No!

> *Tess* pulls away, taking the bag with her. She turns from Alec and puts her bag down. She then takes off her hat and gloves, places the gloves in the hat, and puts the hat on the bag. As she is doing this, the **Chorus** enter on their lines to take up positions around the raised areas, and **Alec** prowls restlessly around Tess.

Chorus 1	She arrives at Trantridge –
Alec	A kiss, cousin.
Chorus 2	Begins her work on the farm –
Alec	It's not much to ask.
Chorus 3	Her new life begins, the weeks pass –
Alec	We're kinsfolk, aren't we?
Chorus 4	And wherever she turns, he's always there –
Alec	What harm can there be?
Chorus 5	Sweet-tongued, cajoling –
Alec	One kiss between cousins.
Chorus 6	Pleading, persuading –
Alec	That's all I ask.
Chorus 7	Her handsome master, her own Prince Charming –
Alec	There'll be no harm.
Chorus 8	Desperate to woo her, desperate to win her –
Alec	Nobody will know.

Chorus 9	Determined to have her all for his own.
Alec	Nobody will see.

Car, Nancy and *Lizzie Darch* enter on the opposite side of the stage. They watch as *Alec* takes *Tess* by the shoulders, and swings her round to him. Instinctively, angrily, *Tess* tries to slap his face, but he grabs her hand, stopping her. *Alec* stares at Tess in fury, and it seems for a moment he might do her some terrible harm. But instead, he leans forward, and kisses her, very gently, on the forehead. He smiles, gives a little bow, turns from her, picks up her bag, gloves and hat, and walks off. *Car, Nancy* and *Lizzie Darch* speak mockingly. Their words are directed at Tess.

Car	Who does she think she is, then?
Nancy	Miss Prim and Proper.
Lizzie	Miss High and Mighty.
Car	Turning her face with a maiden's blush.
Nancy	Butter wouldn't melt in her mouth.
Car	Just who does she think – ?
Nancy	Who does she think – ?
All Three	Who does she think she is?

Tess approaches the women.

Tess	My name's Tess Durbeyfield – I work at Trantridge.
Car	We know who you are.
Nancy	And who you work for.
Tess	I thought I'd come into town tonight.

Lizzie	Very good of you to grace us with your presence.
Tess	I've seen you before – but I don't know your names.
Car	Car Darch.
Nancy	Nancy Darch.
Lizzie	Lizzie Darch.
Tess	I'm pleased to meet you.

Car, Nancy and *Lizzie move around Tess, weaving paths in and out, like predators circling their prey. **Tess** gradually becomes more and more nervous.*

Car	You think you're someone, don't you?
Nancy	Just 'cos you've caught the master's eye.
Lizzie	You think you're the gleam in the master's eye.
Car	We've seen that gleam in the master's eye.
Nancy	You really think that you're the first?
Lizzie	You're not the first, and you won't be the last.
Nancy	You really think –
Lizzie	You really think –
All Three	You really think you're someone.
Tess	*(Protesting)* I don't think anything like that. I've just come here to work.
Car	Do you think that's why you've been brought here?
Nancy	That's not why he's brought you here.
Lizzie	We know why he's brought you here.

Car	And it's not from the goodness of his heart.
Nancy	That one there hasn't got a heart.
Lizzie	You'll find out why before too long.
Car	And then you'll be singing –
Nancy	And then you'll be singing –
All Three	We'll hear you singing a different song.

*Music plays. The **Darch** women and the **Chorus** sing in a coarse and boisterous manner. During the song, **Tess** moves towards the back of the stage, away from the others, attempting to escape their attention.*

Darches/Chorus

There once was a maid, and a fair maid was she,
Went to work for the son of a high family.
And he said to the maid, 'You're the fairest I've seen,
And just right for working my threshing machine.'

She was the fairest that he'd ever seen,
And he taught her to work on his threshing machine.

'Oh, sir,' says the maid, 'of this I'm not sure,
For threshing is work that I've not done before.'
Said he to the maid, 'If you'll come with me now,
And climb up beside me, then I'll show you how.'

She was the fairest that he'd ever seen,
And he taught her to work on his threshing machine.

They threshed all the day, they threshed all the night,
Till the maid got the hang of the workings all right.
And when the sun rose on them both the next day,
The two of them there were still threshing away.

She was the fairest that he'd ever seen,
And he taught her to work on his threshing machine.

__Alec__ enters, bringing the song to an end.

Alec	What the devil is all this row about?
Car	Just having a bit of fun, master.
Nancy	You'll allow us a bit of fun in town on a Saturday night.
Lizzie	You're not against having a bit of fun yourself, are you?
Alec	That's enough. It's late. It's time you were going back. There's work to be done tomorrow.
Car	But it's Sunday tomorrow.
Alec	And there's still harvesting to be done, whatever the day of the week it is, and I want you all up early and in the fields. And anyone that isn't can look to someone else to pay their wages. Now, get along, all of you.

> *Car, Lizzie and Nancy move away, but do not leave the stage. The Chorus return to their positions by the raised areas. Alec catches sight of Tess.*

Alec	Tess! You're here as well?
Tess	Yes, sir.
Alec	I didn't think these Saturday night frolics were to your taste.
Nancy	No. She's too high and mighty for that.
Tess	I thought I might come along with them tonight – just to see – but I don't think I shall be coming again.
Alec	Very wise. You'd do best to stay clear of it. It's not for you.
Lizzie	No. It's another kind of frolic he's got in mind for her.
Tess	I'll be getting along, now.
Alec	You don't intend to go back with them, surely? It's three miles.

Tess   I don't mind the walk.

Alec   But you'll mind the company. And I know a shorter route.

Tess   I don't know…

Alec   Please, cousin. Allow me the honour of escorting you home.

There is a pause.

Tess   All right. Thank you.

Alec holds out his arm to Tess. She hesitates, then takes it. They turn from the others.

Car   Out of the frying pan, into the fire.

Nancy   Straight into the devil's den.

Lizzie   And she can expect to get burned before the night's done.

Car, Nancy and Lizzie go, laughing. The lights dim. The Chorus narrate as Alec and Tess walk slowly around one of the raised areas and back to centre stage.

Chorus 1   It's a warm September night –

Chorus 2   The moon full, the smell of summer fading –

Chorus 3   As they leave the road, walk across the shining fields –

Chorus 4   Footsteps whispering in the wet grass –

Chorus 5   Following a path to dark trees –

Chorus 6   The path of her fortune, her destiny's track –

Chorus 7   Whose design was fixed at her star's birth.

Tess and *Alec* stand centre stage. *Tess* looks
around.

Tess	What place is this?
Alec	The Chase. It's the oldest wood in England. Our way lies through here.
Tess	*(Moving away from Alec)* I want to go back.
Alec	Back? Where?
Tess	Into the open – to the road.
Alec	The road's miles behind us, now. And I doubt you'd find your way back to it on your own. I'm afraid this is the only path you can take.
Tess	*(Angrily)* You've played me false!
Alec	No, Tess. It's you that have played me false.
Tess	What do you mean?
Alec	You show me no favour, no gratitude –

Tess	Why should I?
Alec	Didn't I take you in? Didn't I give you employment?
Tess	Yes…
Alec	I've done everything I can to help you and your family. Your father has a new horse, your brothers and sisters have toys to play with. You might say I've been your guardian angel. Now, don't I deserve a little thanks in return?
Tess	I am grateful.
Alec	Then show it!
Tess	How?
Alec	*(Moving in close to her)* By not being so… cold towards me. I'm not that hateful to you, am I?
Tess	No. You're not hateful.
Alec	And you do like me?
Tess	I like you, well enough.
Alec	And, perhaps, you might also come to love me. Tell me, Tess, truthfully. Do you love me, just a little?
	Tess is confused, she doesn't know how to reply to this.
Alec	Let me have a kiss, cousin.
Tess	No!
Alec	*(Turning from her, angrily)* I've had enough of this! For three months, now, you've snubbed me, scorned me –
Tess	Scorned you?
Alec	Yes! You know how I feel about you! Yet every time I come near you, or try to speak to you, you turn from me, push me away. And I won't stand for it any longer!

Alec changes his tone abruptly, and speaks kindly.

Alec   You're shivering.

Tess   It's cold.

Alec   Here. This will keep you warm.

Alec takes off his coat, and wraps it around Tess. He lifts her face towards him.

Alec   Just one kiss, Tess. That's all. We're hidden here. No one can see. One kiss, no more. And who's to know?

Alec and Tess remain still, frozen, looking at each other. The Chorus, facing outwards, form a circle about them. They speak as they move, their voices building to a crescendo.

Chorus 1   The trees close about them –

Chorus 2   The wood wraps them in its black shadows –

Chorus 3   The ancient woodland, of oak, ash and thorn –

Chorus 4   Where the owl sweeps down on silent wings –

Chorus 5   The fox follows the track of its prey –

Chorus 6   The weasel sniffs out the smell of blood –

Chorus 1 – 3   The place of the talon –

Chorus 1 – 6   The place of the claw –

Chorus 1 – 9   The place of hunger, the hunt and the kill!

The Chorus turn in to face Tess and Alec. Blackout.

. . . .

Scene 3

A single light rises on Joan, who is standing at the side of the stage. She speaks to the audience. As she speaks, the lights rise slowly to reveal Tess, standing, centre stage. She stares straight ahead, her face expressionless.

Joan   When I saw her standing there at the door, I knew that something was wrong. I hardly needed for her to tell me what had happened. Of course, anybody else would have got him to marry her, after that – anybody but her. The girl always had too much pride and too little sense. I had such high hopes when she went up there. Now she's back, with no husband and no future, and her father sick at heart, and me having to scrape and slave. Such hopes, and see what they've come to. The girl should have been more careful if she didn't mean to get him to make her his wife!

Tess turns on Joan.

Tess   How could I know, Mother? I was child when I left here, and I knew nothing. You should have warned me, you should have told me what it was I was going to, but you didn't. You told me nothing!

Joan cannot reply to this. She goes. Abraham and Liza-Lu enter. Abraham carries a jug filled with water. Liza-Lu carries a baby wrapped in a shawl. Tess takes the baby from Liza-Lu, and nurses it. The villagers, Rachel and Sarah enter, to stand, as before, either side of the stage.

Villager 1   It's the old story.

Villager 2   We've heard it before, and we'll hear it again.

Rachel   A pity it had to happen to her, though.

Villager 3   It's always the pretty ones. The plain ones are as safe as a church.

Villager 4	At least there'll be no more of that d'Urberville nonsense. Plain Durbeyfield will have to do for her from now on.
Villager 1	If she'd have made do with that from the start, maybe she wouldn't have the trouble she's got now.
Villager 2	It's a lesson to be learned. 'Seek and ye shall find.' But what you find ain't always what you went looking for.
Villager 3	It's certain she came back with a bit more than she reckoned on.
Sarah	But she's a mindful mother, and seems fond of the child.
Villager 4	I had a glance at it the other day. It's a weak, sickly thing, and not long for the churchyard.

*The **villagers** go. **Rachel** and **Sarah** remain.*

Abraham	He's stopped crying, Tess.
Tess	Yes. He's quieter now.
Liza-Lu	Does that mean he's getting better?
Tess	No, Liza-Lu. He's not getting better. And I fear he'll never cry again.
Abraham	Oh, Tess!

***Abraham** starts to cry.*

Tess	Don't weep, Abraham. It's a sad world that he was born into, and there should be no sadness in his dying out of it.
Abraham	A blighted world?
Tess	Yes. A blighted world.
Liza-Lu	Isn't there anything we can do?
Tess	There's one thing, perhaps. If we can't save his body, at least we can send his poor soul to heaven.

Liza-Lu	Do you mean to christen him?
Tess	I do.
Liza-Lu	But that must be done by the parson.
Tess	There isn't time to fetch the parson. We'll have to do it ourselves. And if God has any mercy he won't turn his face from a little child that's done no harm in the world.
Abraham	What are you going to name him?
Tess	I've thought of that. I'll name him 'Sorrow'.

*Tess kneels, followed by **Liza-Lu** and **Abraham.***

Tess	Sorrow, I baptize thee, in the name of the Father, and of the Son, and of the Holy Ghost.

Tess sprinkles water from the jug over the baby. Then, tenderly, lovingly, she raises the child up in her arms.

Tess	Oh God, accept this child. Heap as much anger as you want upon me, and welcome. But pity my poor baby!

She lowers the child to the floor.

Tess	It's done. It's over.

John enters, and stands apart.

John	Mercy and pity God might have, but that parson has none. Not allowing the child a Christian burial, putting the poor creature in the ground outside the church walls, among the nettles and the weeds. It was that more than anything broke her heart. He won't see me in his church no more.

*He holds out his hand to **Abraham** and*
***Liza-Lu.** They rise, cross to him, and the*
*three of them go. **Rachel** and **Sarah** pick up*
*their props and move to Tess. **Rachel** carries*
the crown of flowers worn earlier by Tess,
***Sarah,** the willow wand she held. As they*
speak, they hand the flowers and willow
*wand to **Tess.***

Sarah   And to think how we danced last year on the green.

Rachel   How we laughed in the sunlight, and it cast no shadow.

Sarah   And she with her crown of flowers, her feet stepping on the
green earth, in the spring of the year.

Rachel   And placing now those same flowers on the cold earth of her
child's grave.

Sarah   Her own childhood's grave.

Rachel   As the wind bites.

Sarah   And the year turns old.

*   **Rachel** and **Sarah** go. **Tess** places the*
flowers and willow wand on the body of the
child. The lights fade on her slowly to
darkness.

. . . .

Act 2

• • • • • • •

Scene 1

*The lights rise on **Joan** and **Tess**. **Tess** is wearing a white dress. **Joan** stands to one side of the stage. **Tess** sits on one of the raised areas, head down.*

Joan   For two years she lived on in the village, staying clear of others, keeping herself to herself. The talk about her soon died down, and her misfortune was forgotten, but I knew she could never be happy here again, and that in the end it would be best for her to go away. So I wrote to an old friend of mine from the south, near Egdon Heath, and found her a place at Talbothays Dairy House. It was where I grew up as a girl, where my own folk came from. And perhaps there, I thought, in the country of her kin, she could make a new life for herself, and put behind her the sorrow she'd found here.

***Joan** goes. **Tess** stands and takes up a central position towards the back of the stage, facing forward, as the **Chorus** enter on their lines, moving to occupy the spaces on and around the two raised areas.*

Chorus 1   By cart from Marlott to Stourcastle –

Chorus 2   By carrier's van through Abbots Cerne and Flintcomb-Ash –

Chorus 3   Between the hills of Bulbarrow and High Stoy, Tess takes the road south –

Chorus 4   Dismounting at Weatherbury, then on foot, by way of Kingsbere –

Chorus 5   Where her ancestors lie in their rags and bones –

Chorus 6   And crossing to the lowlands of Egdon Heath –

Chorus 7   Where, in ancient times, King Lear went mad –

Chorus 8   To reach, at last, her destination –

Chorus 9	The rich, rolling valley of the Great Dairies.
	Tess walks forwards a little, stops, looks up and around, and speaks.
Tess	It's a May evening, the light's deep and soft. Birds are singing, and I can smell the scent of thyme and sweet grass.
Chorus 1	Below her, the whole valley shines –
Chorus 2	Lit by the sparkling jewels of the river –
Chorus 3	And the breeze carries the gentle voices of the cattle –
Chorus 4	Their horns crowned with wreaths of breath –
Chorus 5	Udders swinging fat sackfuls of milk –
Chorus 6	Big-eyed, warm-tongued, the earth's kind mothers.
	Tess moves further forward, which brings her to front centre stage.
Tess	And everything's so tender and still, so calm and restful, I feel my heart leap and my spirit rise, and I know that everything's going to be all right, and I walk down towards where the cattle are grazing.
Chorus 7	As the valley opens its green arms –
Chorus 8	Welcomes its daughter back to her birthright –
Chorus 9	The place of plenty, the place of healing.
	Mr Crick enters, carrying a stack of wooden buckets. Mrs Crick is with him. She carries a pail of milk and a cup.
Mr Crick	Tess Durbeyfield, is it?
Tess	Yes, sir.
	Mr Crick puts down the buckets.

Mr Crick	I'm Mr Crick, the dairyman here. This is Mrs Crick.
Mrs Crick	*(Putting down the pail and approaching Tess)* Your mother wrote to me about you. I haven't seen her since we were young women together. I hope she's well, and the rest of your family?
Tess	They're very well, thank you, ma'am.

> *During the following,* **Jonathan, Marian, Izz, Retty,** *and* **Angel Clare** *enter, and take up the buckets to prepare for milking.*

Mr Crick	I'm glad to have you here. We've a big herd and it's a busy time just now.
Tess	I hope to prove myself useful to you, Mr Crick.
Mr Crick	As long as you can milk them clean. I don't want any of my cows drying up this time of year.
Tess	You've no worry about that. I know the work well enough.
Mrs Crick	You'll be wanting something to eat after your journey.
Tess	I'll just take a drink of milk, if I may, before I set to work.
Mrs Crick	You can have that, sure enough. *(She calls)* Jonathan! Bring Tess Durbeyfield here a cup of milk.
Jonathan	Yes, Mrs Crick.

> **Jonathan** *takes the cup from Mrs Crick and fills it from the pail.*

Mr Crick	It's all well and good if you can swallow it. I can't stomach the stuff myself.

> **Jonathan** *gives the milk to Tess.*

Jonathan	Here you are, miss. It's still warm.

> **Tess** *takes the milk and drinks.*

Mr Crick	This is Jonathan Kail, one of my dairymen. And here we have the maids – Izz Huett, Marian Hardy, and Retty Priddle.

*The **dairymaids** all nod to Tess.*

Mrs Crick	You'll be sharing your lodgings with them above the dairyhouse.
Jonathan	And fine company you'll be keeping, as well. Retty's a member of the nobility.
Mrs Crick	Now, don't start on at the girl about that again.
Jonathan	It's true, ain't it, Mr Crick?
Mr Crick	So I've heard tell.
Jonathan	*(To Retty)* What was your ancestors again?
Marian	Leave off teasing her, Jonathan.
Jonathan	What was they, Mr Crick?
Mr Crick	The Paridelles, I think it was –
Mrs Crick	You've no call to go encouraging him, either, Richard.
Jonathan	The Paridelles, that's right, a grand family, and they used to own all the land hereabouts in times gone by.
Retty	And those times are long gone, Jonathan Kail, and it don't signify nothing! Not to me, at any rate.
Jonathan	Only since you heard Mr Clare saying how he couldn't abide old families.

***Retty** kicks Jonathan on the leg.*

Mr Crick	No more of that, Retty!
Izz	He only got what was coming to him.
Mrs Crick	She's in the right of it, Richard. It was Jonathan began it.

Mr Crick	All right. Come along, now. Enough of this skylarking. Time to set to work. There's cows to be milked before sunset.

> *Izz, Retty, Marian, Mrs Crick, and Jonathan exit, taking the buckets and the cup with them. Angel starts to follow them.*

Mr Crick	Mr Clare. You'll be introduced to our new dairymaid?

> *Angel stops and turns.*

Angel	Of course. *(He approaches Tess)* Delighted to meet you, Miss…
Tess	Durbeyfield. Tess Durbeyfield.
Angel	Angel Clare.

> *They shake hands. Angel turns back to Mr Crick.*

Angel	Well. As Mr Crick says, there are cows to be milked. If my hands can ever get used to it.
Mr Crick	You will, sir. But you must take it gently. It's the knack, not the strength, that does it.

> *Mr Crick and Angel go. Tess turns and speaks to the audience.*

Tess	I knew I'd seen him somewhere before, but I didn't know where from. It was only later, when we were working together, that it came to me. That Maytime at Marlott, three years ago. He was the gentleman who came along and danced with Rachel and Sarah. He danced with them, and he'd have danced with me if he'd stayed… but he didn't. He went away, and although I still remembered him, I could see that he didn't know me, or remember who I was.

> *As the Chorus narrate the next section, one group crosses the stage to join the other group on and around a single raised area.*

*Then, **Izz, Retty** and **Marian** enter and step onto the now free raised area, and **Tess** moves across to join them. Finally, **Angel** enters, moving to the centre of the stage.*

Chorus 1   And when the cows have been milked and put in their stalls –

Chorus 2   When supper's been eaten and the sun begins to set –

Chorus 3   Restless in their room above the milkhouse –

Chorus 4   The dairymaids gaze out into the dreaming dusk –

Chorus 5   Where a lone figure stands in the empty yard –

Chorus 6   Face lit by the hazy half-light –

Chorus 7   Their hearts' ache –

Chorus 8   Their souls' pain –

Chorus 9   Their young loves' longing.

*Angel takes out a penny whistle and plays a tune. The **dairymaids** gaze down lovingly at him. He stops playing, takes out a book, and reads.*

Marian   He's a real gentleman, a parson's son.

Izz   His father's the Reverend Clare from Emminster.

Retty   All his sons are parsons, except for Mr Clare.

Marian   He's studying how to be a farmer.

Izz   Clever, he is, and always reading.

Retty   Keeps himself to himself, and never says much to us.

Marian   Too much taken up with his own thoughts.

Izz   He hardly even knows we're here.

Retty	But he does play the whistle beautiful.
Tess	Why should he want to be a farmer? Why isn't he a parson, like his brothers?

Angel closes his book, looks up, and speaks to the audience.

Angel	Because it was destined for me, and I rebel against destiny. A man must learn to shape his own destiny – even if it brings him into conflict with his parents' desires.

Reverend and Mrs Clare enter and approach Angel. Their conversation takes place in a flashback scene.

Rev. Clare	You prefer not to take Orders?
Angel	That's right, Father.
Mrs Clare	What do you mean by this, Angel?
Angel	What I say, Mother. I have no desire to follow my brothers into the church.
Rev. Clare	I must confess, Angel, this is something of a shock.
Angel	I am sorry for that. I've no wish to distress you.
Rev. Clare	Nevertheless, you do!
Mrs Clare	Your father has devoted his life to serving the church. And it has always been his earnest desire – our desire – to see all our children do likewise.
Angel	I know, Mother. And I know your devotion to the church springs from a deep and honest love. But it's a love I do not, and cannot share –
Mrs Clare	Angel –
Angel	– not while I find its creeds too narrow for my own thoughts and desires.

Rev. Clare	Too narrow!
Angel	Yes.
Rev. Clare	You think I am narrow?
Angel	Not you, Father – but to my mind, God need not only be sought within the confines of the church –
Rev. Clare	Enough of this!
Angel	– but also in the life of the natural world, and in the soul of man –
Rev. Clare	I will not hear it!
Angel	Then perhaps I was wrong. Perhaps you have grown narrow –
Mrs Clare	Angel! How dare you speak to your father like that!

There is a pause.

Angel	I'm sorry. I apologize, Father.
Rev. Clare	Angel. You are my youngest son, and I can see that I have made that mistake which many parents make with children born to them in their later years. I have been too liberal with you… too indulgent… I planted the seed of this rebellion in you, and now I am reaping its bitter harvest.

Reverend Clare turns and walks off.

Mrs Clare	What do you intend to do, Angel?
Angel	I don't know, yet.
Mrs Clare	You have no course in mind?
Angel	None at all.
Mrs Clare	You know we're not rich – but the money we have managed to save, which was to send you to university –
Angel	And which is out of the question, now!

Mrs Clare	I'm sure that it can be used to… assist you along whatever path you do eventually decide to take.
Angel	Thank you, Mother.
Mrs Clare	And I hope and pray, for your sake, it's a path that will lead to your happiness.

Mrs Clare goes, ending the flashback.
Angel speaks to the audience.

Angel	I left home, and went up to London, but I found nothing there – except a rather sordid and short-lived romantic affair, of which the less said the better. Town life was distasteful to me. It was the country I liked, there I felt most at ease and at home. And the thought came to me that I should take up farming – here, perhaps, or even abroad. And the more I considered it, the more I knew I'd found my chosen path. So, I began a course of open-air studies, which concluded in my arriving at Talbothays Dairy, where I was due to stay until the autumn, before leaving to take up my chosen career.
Marian	And if he's to be a farmer –
Izz	He'll want himself a wife –
Retty	A man like that must have a wife –
Marian	And not a gentle-born, fine-bred lady wife –
Izz	Fit only for tea-parties and greeting guests –
Retty	But a good, honest, hard-working farmer's wife –
Marian	Who can milk cows and churn good butter –
Izz	Who knows the value of the land and the beasts that live off it –
Retty	If he takes a wife, that's the kind of wife he'll take –
Marian	And each one of us would be that wife –
Izz	If he asked us, we wouldn't think twice –

Retty	We'd be willing and happy to be that wife.

Angel plays his whistle again. Tess steps down from the raised area and moves towards him. He hears her, and stops playing.

Angel	Who's that?
Tess	It's just me, sir.
Angel	*(Turning to her)* Tess?
Tess	I'm sorry…
Angel	Sorry for what?
Tess	I didn't mean to disturb you.
Angel	You didn't.
Tess	I just… I heard the music…
Angel	I'm still learning.
Tess	You make a sweet sound.
Angel	Thank you.
Tess	I'd better go…
Angel	You don't have to.
Tess	It's late, and we must be up early tomorrow.
Angel	I suppose you're right. Well, then. Goodnight, Tess.

Tess	Goodnight, sir.
Angel	Please, don't call me that. We're all equal here, aren't we? No distinctions of class, no sirs or ma'ams. Just Tess Durbeyfield and Angel Clare.
Tess	Very well. Goodnight… Mr Clare.

*Tess goes. **Angel** looks after her. The **dairymaids** speak with sad resignation.*

Marian	What's the use of fooling ourselves?
Izz	If there was a chance for any of us before –
Retty	There's no chance for any of us now –
Marian	Because from the moment when we first saw how he looked at her –
Izz	And how it was she looked at him –
Retty	And how something, even then, passed between them –
Marian	We knew there was only one way of it –
Izz	That the two of them were meant to be brought together –
Retty	And, all in all, it was only a matter of time.

All freeze on stage as lights dim to blackout.

· ·

Scene 2

*The lights come up bright. **Mr Crick** and **Jonathan** enter carrying a large butter barrel and paddle which they place centre stage. **Mrs Crick** accompanies them. **Jonathan** takes the paddle and stirs it round the barrel. It is hard work. **Izz, Marian, Retty,** and **Angel** gather round to watch. **Tess** enters and joins them as the **Chorus** speak.*

Chorus 1	And time passes, and the days run together –
Chorus 2	The flow of life and the flow of work on the land –
Chorus 3	Skimming milk in the cool of the early mornings –
Chorus 4	Herding the cattle out to pasture –
Chorus 5	The purr of the milk into the pail –
Chorus 6	The green heat of the valley –
Chorus 7	Hoof-drum, tail-swish –
Chorus 8	Slow talk, soft laughter –
Chorus 9	The heart's blood warming with the summer's heat.

Jonathan stops stirring. He looks inside the barrel.

Jonathan	The butter's still not taken, Mr Crick.
Mr Crick	I can't understand it. We haven't had this happen in years. What might be the cause of it, do you think?
Jonathan	There's only one person can divine that for you. Conjurer Trendle, over on Egdon Heath.
Mr Crick	I don't set no store by conjurers and their like.
Marian	My mother had a wart on her hand that nothing would move, so she went to Conjurer Trendle for a cure, and it was gone within a month.
Izz	It's said he can forecast the weather, as well.
Jonathan	And he makes up love-potions. Perhaps you ought to go and see him for one, Retty.
Retty	I'll be going to see him for a curse to bind your tongue, if you don't shut up!

Mr Crick	That's enough! It's not right to have such pagan talk going on with a parson's son present.
Angel	Don't mind me. I have an open mind on these matters. In fact, such things quite intrigue me. 'There are more things in heaven and earth', you know.
Mrs Crick	There are, Mr Clare, it's true. And I have heard it said that somebody in the house being in love can be the cause.
Jonathan	We haven't got to look no further than Retty, then!

Retty hits out at Jonathan, but he ducks away.

Mr Crick	You might have found out the reason, Alice. Do you remember that maid we had, years ago? The butter wouldn't churn then.
Mrs Crick	Rebecca Brook, do you mean?
Mr Crick	That's the girl. She was in love.
Mrs Crick	It's true, she was. But it wasn't her being in love that stopped the butter from churning. It was the man she was in love with.

Mrs Crick tells her story to the others.

Mrs Crick	Jack Dollop was his name. He was a milker here, and one for the maids, if you take my meaning. He was courting young Rebecca at the time, and she being an innocent maid and knowing nothing of men, he didn't find it hard to turn her head, just as he'd turned the heads of many another before her.

Jack and Rebecca enter, to front centre stage. They enact Mrs Crick's story. Their performance should be highly stylized and mannered, as in a melodrama or farce.

Rebecca	It's all right, isn't it, Jack?
Jack	Course it's all right, Becky.
Rebecca	You do mean to marry me, don't you?
Jack	Haven't I told you so?

Rebecca	Shouldn't we wait, then, till we are married?
Jack	But who knows when that day will be? And, until it arrives, surely we should seal our true love with a solemn and sacred vow.
Rebecca	And is that what it is, Jack? A sacred vow?
Jack	There's nothing more sacred, my dear.
Rebecca	And… nothing will come of it?
Jack	Nothing at all. I give you my word – as I give you my heart.
Rebecca	Then I will, Jack! I will!
Jack	Oh, my love! Let us delay this vow-taking no longer!

Jack drags Rebecca off-stage, hurriedly.

Mrs Crick	In short, he deceived her, poor, simple creature that she was. And he'd have gone on deceiving her as well, if nature hadn't taken its course, and brought Becky's folly to the light of day. And if she hadn't had the mother she had.

Off-stage, Mrs Brook shouts, angrily.

Mrs Brook	Where is he? Where is the villain!

Jack comes running on-stage in a panic.

Jack	Mr Crick! Mr Crick! I have to hide!
Mr Crick	Hide? From what?

Mrs Brook bellows, off-stage.

Mrs Brook	Jack Dollop! Are you in there?
Jack	From her! She'll murder me!

Mrs Brook bellows again, off-stage.

Mrs Brook	I have a bone to pick with you, and it ain't a small one, neither!

Mrs Crick	And fearing for his very life, he hid in the only place he thought was safe – the butter barrel.

> *Jack climbs into the barrel, hides, then pops his head out again.*

Jack	For mercy's sake, Mr Crick, don't tell her where I am!

> *Mr Crick pushes Jack's head back down.*

Mrs Crick	And only just in time, for the next second, Mrs Brook came storming in here, wielding the biggest brass-handled umbrella you ever saw, and with Rebecca in tow.

> *Mrs Brook enters, a formidable figure wielding a large umbrella, and followed by a shamefaced and weeping Rebecca.*

Mrs Brook	*(To Mr Crick)* Does Jack Dollop work here?
Mr Crick	He does. Who wants him?
Mrs Brook	I want him. Is he here?
Mr Crick	As you can see –
Mrs Brook	He's hiding. He must be. I'll find him, and when I do I'll claw his face for him!

> *Mrs Brook calls out.*

Mrs Brook	Jack Dollop! You scoundrel! You lecherous young rapscallion! Where are you? I've got Becky here with me and she's feeling none too happy on account of you. Becky! Let him hear how distressed you are.

> *Rebecca howls, loudly.*

Mrs Brook	You hear that, Jack Dollop? I'm giving you one last warning, you slack-twisted villain! Come out here this minute and make reparation for the violation you've done, or I promise you, after I've caught you, you'll be nothing more than a sackful of broken bones!

Mrs Brook searches the stage for Jack Dollop.

Mrs Crick	She searched here.
Mr Crick	And she searched there.
Mrs Crick	She searched high.
Mr Crick	And she searched low.
Mrs Crick	But she couldn't find that Jack Dollop anywhere.
Mr Crick	Until, at last, her eye fell on the butter barrel.

Mrs Brook creeps up to the barrel, then raises her umbrella and brings it down with a crash.

Mrs Brook Jack Dollop! I know you're in there. Come out now and make your promise, and I promise not to raise a hand against you. *(There is no reply)* No? Well, then. You've had fair warning!

Mrs Brook takes hold of the paddle and stirs it round inside the barrel.

Mrs Crick And she took hold of the paddle and round and round she paddled it, with Jack Dollop hollering and shouting inside.

Jack calls from inside the barrel.

Jack Stop it! Let me out! I'll be churned into a pulp! Stop!

Mrs Brook Not till you make amends for ravaging poor Becky's virgin innocence!

Jack Stop paddling, you old witch!

Mrs Brook Old witch, do you call me? It's mother-in-law you should've been calling me these last five months!

Jack Please! Let me out!

Mrs Brook Do you promise to make it right with her?

Jack	I promise.
Mrs Brook	Within the month?
Jack	Within a week, if you'll just stop!
Mrs Brook	Then out you come.

She stops paddling. **Jack** *climbs out.* **Mrs Brook** *grabs him with one hand, and grabs her daughter with the other.*

Mrs Crick	And out he came, mazed and dazed and his legs turned to jelly, and Mrs Brook takes her daughter by one hand, and Jack Dollop by another, and she says –

Mrs Brook *clasps Jack and Rebecca's hands together.*

Mrs Brook	What God hath joined, let no man put asunder. Or he'll have me to deal with!

Still holding onto both of them, **Mrs Brook** *marches them off-stage.* **Mr Crick** *and* **Jonathan** *carry the barrel to the side of the stage.*

Mrs Crick	And he was true to his word and married the girl a week later. Which just goes to show that, contrary to what some folks believe, there is natural justice at work in the world.
Jonathan	*(Returning)* I don't know about natural justice. Looks to me like there weren't much in the way of justice for Jack Dollop.
Marian	What do you mean? It was only natural and fair he should be made to make amends for what he'd done to the maid.
Jonathan	What he'd done to her? Do you mean to say there was no doing on her part?
Izz	Only after she'd been persuaded to with lies and deceits.

Retty	And that's usually the way of it.
Jonathan	To my way of thinking, there's a lot less persuading needs to be done than is let on to, and there's many an innocent man been trapped into marriage by a knowing maid –

Tess suddenly turns on Jonathan furiously.

Tess	And what would you know about it, Jonathan Kail? A woman can be charmed by soft words and empty promises – a woman who might not be much more than a girl, and who knows little of the ways of men – she can be charmed and bewitched into betraying her own self – and it's the man who can walk away afterwards, and the woman who is left to pay the consequences!

They all stare at Tess in silence. She turns and walks away from them, to stand separately.

Jonathan	I didn't mean nothing by it –
Izz	You never do.
Jonathan	I was just saying –
Retty	And it could be that sometimes you just say too much!

Retty, Izz, Marian, and Jonathan go.

Mr Crick	I hope nothing's the matter with her.
Mrs Crick	I noticed she was looking a bit flushed this morning. She may have been working a bit too hard.
Mr Crick	She's a hard worker, all right.
Mrs Crick	Well, perhaps you can make do without her today, Richard. Give her time to recover her health and her spirits.

Mr and Mrs Crick go. Angel remains on-stage. He plays a slow tune on his whistle. He stops as Tess sings to the tune.

Tess

My love is fair, his eyes are blue.
He came to me when the moon was new.
The earth was green, the sun was warm.
And he laid his head upon my arm.

Angel

You know the song?

Tess

Yes. My mother taught it to me when I was a young girl.

*Angel plays again and **Tess** sings with him.*

Tess

Now the moon is full and the year is old.
The days are short, and the earth is cold.
And the rain it falls without a sound.
And my love he lies beneath the ground.

The song ends.

Angel

It's a sad song.

Tess

I like sad songs. To my mind, they're the natural voice of the
world.

*Angel holds out his hand to Tess. She
hesitates, then takes it, and they walk
together across to the unoccupied raised
area, and sit down. The **Chorus** speak.*

Chorus 1

These are the times when they meet –

Chorus 2

In the late summer evenings when the sun is sinking –

Chorus 3

Or in the early summer mornings, before the sun's rising –

Chorus 4

When the light is soft with pale mists –

Chorus 5

The two of them alone in the shining world –

Chorus 6

Like the first two ever to walk in that world.

Angel

Is the world a sad place do you think, Tess?

Tess

It seems to be at times. Sad, and fearful.

Angel	But not at all times.
Tess	No. There are other times when you can sense something beyond you, a kind of spirit, in the trees and the hills and the rivers. *(She loses herself in her vision)* And this spirit, you know it's part of you as well, and you're part of it. And it never dies, and you'll never die, because it is the spirit that moves through all things, and makes them one.

> **Tess** *recovers herself, and turns to Angel, a little embarrassed.*

Tess	I suppose you find such thinking foolish.
Angel	Not at all. I've thought it myself – and felt it. But never so strongly as here, and now.

> **Tess** *stands, and moves away a little, lost in her own thoughts.*

Tess	When I was a little girl, I used to go out sometimes at night and lie on my back on the grass and look up at the stars. So many of them, all glittering and shining in the dark. And the more I looked at them, the more I saw, going on and on, into forever. And I'd feel myself lift up out of my body, and rise away from the earth, and I'd be out there among them, out among the stars. I was never so happy as I was then.
Chorus 1	And there, in the moon-hazy twilight of the evening –
Chorus 2	Or the speckled, pollen-gold twilight of the morning –
Chorus 3	She's transformed before his eyes –
Chorus 4	A spirit stepped out of the landscape, shimmering with the holy glow of the season –
Chorus 5	Artemis rising from the shining earth.

> **Tess** *turns to Angel.*

Tess	Who?
Angel	Artemis – a divinity of ancient Greece.

Tess	*(Sharply)* I'm no… divinity.
Angel	*(Standing)* I'm sorry – I've offended you.
Tess	No. It's not you.
Angel	What is it, then? What makes you so sad? If you told me –
Tess	*(Quickly)* There's nothing to tell! *(She softens a little)* You know so much. If I knew half as much as you – I dreamed of being a teacher once – but my upbringing was against it.
Angel	If you want to study I could help you.
Tess	No. It's too late for me, now. My life has its course and it must be run.
Angel	We can change our lives, you know. The more we learn –
Tess	Perhaps I don't want to learn more than I've learned already. Except one thing.
Angel	What?

Tess turns to him and speaks with surprising bitterness.

Tess	Why the sun shines on the just and the unjust alike. But I don't think there's any book written can tell me that.

Angel moves to her to comfort her. He turns her to him, and takes her hands. As he does, Retty enters. She stands apart but her eyes are fixed on Tess and Angel. She speaks to the audience.

Retty	We saw the time they spent together, and we saw how the time drew them closer together. And I couldn't say I'd lost him to her, because he'd never been mine. And I couldn't say I hated her, because there was nothing in her to hate. What he loved about her, we loved as well. And though it felt like the best part of me was being killed, I saw with the others what was plain to see. That he liked Tess Durbeyfield, and loved Tess Durbeyfield, and if he meant to marry anyone, he'd marry Tess Durbeyfield.

	Tess cries out, and turns from Angel to Retty.
Tess	No! He won't! He can't. You, Retty, but not me! I'm not the one for him. I won't marry him! I can't!
Chorus 6	That's what she says when he finally asks her –
Tess	*(Back to Angel)* I can't.
Chorus 7	On a July morning after heavy rain –
Tess	*(To Angel)* I won't.
Chorus 8	When the fields are wet and the grass is steaming –
Tess	*(To Angel)* I don't want to marry you. I only want to love you.
Chorus 9	And the river's rising and flooding its banks –
Tess	*(To Angel)* I'd rather be yours than anybody's in the world. But I can't marry you. Don't ask me again. Don't say any more. There's no more to be said.
	Tess goes. Angel remains as he is, looking towards her. The Chorus move on their lines from the raised area, to stand in small groups about the stage.
Chorus 1	But there is, there's a lot more to be said –
Chorus 2	And he does, he does ask her again –
Chorus 3	As July passes and August comes –
Chorus 4	He waits for her to change her mind –
Chorus 5	Because he's certain she'll change her mind –
Chorus 6	After all the whole thing's happened so quickly –
Chorus 7	She's been taken by surprise, all she needs is time –
Chorus 8	But she's the one for him, he knows that for certain –

Chorus 9	And he knows that for certain she's sure to change her mind.

> *Reverend and Mrs Clare enter, to the side of the stage nearest to Angel. Angel turns to face them. They speak to the audience.*

Rev. Clare When Angel informed us of his intentions – of asking this girl to marry him – I have to admit that, at first, we were rather taken aback.

Mrs Clare We had always had it in mind that, when the time came, our son would choose for his partner a young woman more of his own position in society.

Rev. Clare And this young woman, by his own ready admittance, was not that, but a cottager's daughter, a dairymaid.

Mrs Clare And yet, when he explained his reasoning to us – how, as a farmer, it would be far more suitable for him to have a wife who understood the work and the life –

Rev. Clare And when he assured us that she was a most tender, loving, and pure young woman –

Mrs Clare And as our only ambition for Angel was his own welfare and happiness –

Rev. Clare We really had no alternative but to give him – to give them both, even though we had not yet seen the girl –

Mrs Clare Our blessing, and our consent.

> *Angel crosses to them. Reverend Clare shakes his hand. Mrs Clare kisses him. They turn and go. Angel speaks to the audience. Tess enters to stand opposite.*

Angel As we continued working alongside each other, I learned more about her, and she about me. And I discovered that I had seen her before. That she'd been one of the girls I'd seen dancing on the village green at Marlott three years before. The one I hadn't danced with. She wept as she told me. She wept bitterly, and I held her, and her body shook with the weeping.

Angel	And she kept on saying, 'Why didn't you dance with me? You should have danced with me.' Over and over, she said it, as if her heart was breaking.

*Joan and John Durbeyfield enter, to the side of the stage nearest to Tess. **Tess** turns to face them, as if she can see them. They speak to the audience.*

John	She wrote to us about him, this Mr Clare, and how he'd asked her to marry him.
Joan	And I said to myself, thank God she's found someone, and she can put all her misfortunes behind her.
John	And what with him being a parson's son and a gentleman, it seemed an act of providence, her being of high blood herself.
Joan	But as for telling him or even breathing a word to him about her past trouble –
John	Which was never any fault of hers anyhow –
Joan	– only a fool would do such a thing. I wrote back to her, and told her she wasn't even to think of it.
John	She ain't the first or the highest in the land to have such trouble, and if they don't trumpet theirs, why should she trumpet hers?
Joan	For, knowing men as I do, it would be the surest way she could find of losing him.
John	And would bring shame on herself, and her noble family.

*They go. **Tess** turns and speaks to the audience.*

Tess	I knew it wasn't right that I should marry him. Not with my past what it was, not with all that had happened to me. But I knew from the minute he asked me, even as I told him no – even when I was trying my hardest to do what was proper and decent – I knew deep down that in the end it had to be.

Tess	*(Tess and Angel approach each other, to centre stage)* And it happened one time, about the middle of September, when we'd been to take the milk to the station, and we were driving back to the dairy in the cart. He stopped at the top of a hill, and I knew that he was going to ask again, and I knew this time what my answer would be. But even then, despite what Mother had written, even then I tried to do what was right.

Angel takes Tess's hand.

Angel	You must give me a reason. At least grant me that, won't you?
Tess	Yes. *(She hesitates)* It's to do with… what I am… my history…
Angel	Your history? You've told me that.
Tess	Not everything. You see I… I'm not a Durbeyfield… I'm a d'Urberville. An old family that's gone to nothing.
Angel	I've heard of them. What of it?
Tess	That's what it's to do with – with my being a d'Urberville.
Angel	And you know I despise old families?
Tess	Yes, but –
Angel	And you think I'll love you the less for it?
Tess	Not just that…
Angel	What else, then? What else is there to know?

There is a pause.

Tess	Nothing. That's all. There's nothing else.
Angel	Well, then. I can see I shall have to call you Mistress Theresa d'Urberville from now on.
Tess	*(Sharply)* No! Don't use that name. I hate it!

Angel	In that case, there's only one thing for it. If you hate the name so much, you'll have take a new one. Not Theresa d'Urberville... but Mrs Angel Clare.

There is another pause.

Angel	Will you, Tess? Will you take my name?

***Marian, Izz** and **Retty** enter.*

Marian	She's going to marry him.
Izz	Her face shows it.
Retty	*(To Tess)* Are you? Are you going to marry him?

***Tess** turns to them.*

Tess	Yes.

She turns back to Angel.

Tess	Yes, I will.

*Mr and **Mrs Crick** and **Jonathan** enter.
Mr Crick goes to Angel and congratulates him.*

Mr Crick	And I'm truly glad to hear it. I've been watching you two, and I thought you might do such a thing for some time.

***Mrs Crick** goes to Tess.*

Mrs Crick	From the very first day I saw you, I knew you were too good for a dairymaid. Too good and too pretty, and a prize for any man.
Marian	He chose the best of us, Tess, when he chose you.
Izz	We said it was to be, right from the start.

***Retty** moves to Tess, and speaks to her,
fighting back her tears.*

Retty   And we're happy for you… we are, really… and we hope you'll be happy… really, we do…

Jonathan   Don't take on so, Retty. If it's a husband you're looking for, you could do worse than make a match with me.

*This is too much for Retty. She shoots Jonathan a look of anger and pain, then runs back, weeping to the **dairymaids,** who comfort her. **Tess** and **Angel** stand together for the wedding.*

Chorus 1   And so it's done, and, some months later, the wedding takes place –

Chorus 2   *(Stepping forward to place a crown of flowers on Tess's head)* On a cold, sharp New Year's Day –

Chorus 3   In a small village church, where they promise and vow –

Chorus 4   *(Stepping forward, as the vicar, and placing Tess and Angel's hands together)* To love and to cherish, to honour and obey –

Chorus 5   In sickness and health, till death do they part –

Chorus 6   And though there aren't many gathered, those that are gathered –

Chorus 7	All agree that they've never, in all their born days –
Chorus 8	Seen such a handsome or well-matched couple –
Chorus 9	Or a happier groom, or a prettier bride.

> *Music plays.* **Angel** *and* **Tess** *kiss. The* **Chorus** *and others on-stage come forward and congratulate Tess and Angel. Then they make their farewells and leave. The last to go are* **Izz, Marian** *and* **Retty**. **Angel** *kisses* **Izz** *and* **Marian**, *but when he comes to kiss* **Retty** *she can't bear it, and runs off-stage. As this is going on,* **man 1** *and* **man 2** *enter, to one side, and watch.* **Tess** *and* **Angel** *are finally left alone, with only the two* **men** *watching them. As the* **men** *speak to each other,* **Angel** *fetches a travelling bag from behind one of the raised areas, and carries it back towards Tess.*

Man 1	They do make a handsome couple.
Man 2	They do, it's certain.
Man 1	Well-matched, like they said.
Man 2	I don't deny it.
Man 1	He's a lucky man, to have such a fair-looking maid for a wife.
Man 2	Fair-looking she may be, but as to being a maid, I wouldn't be so sure of that –

> **Angel** *turns sharply to* **man 2**. **Tess** *stiffens with shock.*

Angel	What do you mean by that?
Man 2	Sir... ?

> **Angel** *puts down the bag, and approaches* *man 2.*

Angel	You were saying something about my wife.
Man 2	Not me.
Angel	I heard you. And so did she. Now, tell me what you meant by it!
Man 2	I meant nothing.

*Angel hits **man 2**, knocking him down.*

Tess	Angel!
Angel	Will you explain yourself now!

*Man 1 helps **man 2** to his feet.*

Man 1	There's nothing to explain, sir. He's had a bit too much to drink, that's all. And when that happens, he always lets his tongue run away with him.
Man 2	That's right – I meant nothing by it – it was a mistake. I thought she... I thought your wife was somebody else – but I was wrong.
Angel	Perhaps you'd like to apologize, then.
Man 2	Yes, sir... I'm sorry –
Angel	To my wife.

Man 2 goes to Tess.

Man 2	I'm sorry, ma'am. I apologize for thinking you were someone else. You were like her from a distance. But now that we're close up, I can see my mistake.

*Man 2 stares hard at Tess. **Tess** holds his gaze for a while, then turns away.*

Angel	*(To the men)* Now get out!

The men go. Angel stares after them. Tess
remains still, staring away from him. The
lights dim, until only Angel and Tess are
illuminated.

∙ ∙

Scene 3

Tess turns, steps forward, and speaks to the
audience.

Tess   We left Talbothays in the late afternoon and travelled south by
carriage to Wellbridge. It was cold and grey, and the wind blew
sharp from the east. Angel had rented a farmhouse at the
village for our honeymoon, and when we arrived there, he told
me that it had once been part of a grand manor house.

Angel   *(Indicating with his hand)* The property and seat of the
d'Urbervilles. Welcome, Tess, to your ancestral home!

Angel picks up the bag, and walks past Tess
to one of the raised areas. He puts the bag
down and sits.

Tess   The place was dark and damp, but we lit the candles and
made up the fire, and ate the food that had been left for us.
(Tess moves to sit down on the raised area, a little apart from
Angel) We sat on either side of the fire, and there were shadows
around us, a shadow between us. He was gazing into the
flames, and the light flickered across his face. And then he
lifted his head, and looked towards me.

Angel   Tess. I have a confession to make. I should have told you
before – before we were married – but I was afraid.

Tess   You? But –

Angel   Before I tell you, you must promise me one thing.

Tess   What?

Angel	Will you forgive me?
Tess	Of course. Whatever it is.
Angel	Here it is, then. Say nothing till I've finished.

Tess speaks to the audience. *Angel* speaks to
Tess.

Tess	Then he told me how, a few years before, he'd lived for a while in London.
Angel	I was still unsure what direction to take in life, and was in a rather vulnerable state of mind.
Tess	And he'd met a woman there – a woman older than himself – and become involved with her.
Angel	It was foolish – but I was young – and I soon realized what foolishness it was.
Tess	And he broke off the affair –
Angel	– and escaped – not greatly the worse for the experience. And I have never repeated the offence. But you see, Tess, I come to you... sullied by the world. A fallen man. Can you forgive me?

Tess turns to Angel.

Tess	There's nothing to forgive. *(She turns back to the audience)* And now I knew that, at last, I could make my confession, tell him what I'd kept from him all this time. And I was certain he'd forgive me, because, like me, he'd fallen and knew what it was to be damaged by the world. So I looked into his eyes, and I told him.

*Chorus 1 – 5 enter on their lines, to take up
individual positions around the stage.*

Chorus 1	The whole story from beginning to end –
Chorus 2	She tells him it all, leaves nothing out –
Chorus 3	Her soft voice speaking those terrible words –

Chorus 4	And he listens in silence until she's finished –
Chorus 5	And it's all over, and the story's done.

Angel stands.

Angel	Is it true?
Tess	Yes.
Angel	All of it?
Tess	Yes.
Angel	There's nothing more?
Tess	I've told you everything.
Angel	Why didn't you tell me before?
Tess	I tried to…
Angel	But you didn't.
Tess	I wanted to… say you forgive me.
Angel	There was a child.
Tess	Yes.
Angel	And it's dead… but the man… he's still living?
Tess	Yes – and I wish he weren't.
Angel	It would be better if he wasn't.
Tess	Say you forgive me, Angel.
Angel	Is it you? Is it you that's told me this?

*Angel takes hold of **Tess**.*

Angel	Same hair. Same eyes. Same face. But not the same.

Tess	What do you mean?
Angel	You're not her. Not the woman I loved. Not the woman I married.
Tess	I am – I'm the same.
Angel	No, you're not!

> ***Angel** pushes **Tess** away, and turns from her.*

Angel	You'll never be her again!
Tess	I don't understand…
Angel	Something must be done. I must… do something.
Tess	Nothing's changed between us.
Angel	Yes… yes it has… everything.
Tess	I forgave you!
Angel	It's not the same!
Tess	*(Taking his hand)* Angel –
Angel	*(Pulling away from her)* No! Don't touch me!

> ***Angel** moves away.*

Tess	Where are you going?
Angel	I don't blame you. For what happened. It wasn't your fault. I know that. But I can't stay.

> ***Angel** walks off. **Tess** calls after him.*

Tess	Angel!

*The lights dim further. **Chorus 6 – 9** enter on their lines. The full **Chorus** take up positions around Tess, crowding in on her, in a menacing, threatening, phantom-like way.*

Chorus 6   But he's gone, and she stands alone –

Chorus 7   By the dying fire in the empty room –

Chorus 8   And there's no sound at all –

Chorus 9   But the sound of the wind –

Chorus 1   Rising up from the black of the night –

Chorus 2   Sighing round the walls –

Chorus 3   Like lost souls –

Chorus 4   Like all the long-lost souls of the long-dead d'Urbervilles –

Chorus 5   Crowding the window with vampire faces –

Chorus 6   Dead eyes mocking from the grave's deep –

Chorus 7   Hungering towards her for her heart's blood –

Chorus 8   Each tongue whispering the curse that haunts her –

Chorus 9   The name that hangs like a tombstone around her neck –

Chorus 1 – 9   D'Urberville… d'Urberville… d'Urberville…

*The **Chorus** whisper the name, over and over again, until **Tess** silences them with a loud cry of despair and defiance.*

Tess   No!

Sudden blackout.

• •

Act 3

· · · · · · ·

Scene 1

> *The lights rise as **Rachel** and Sarah enter, speaking.*

Sarah   You saw her, here, in Marlott?

Rachel   I did. Right here in the village.

Sarah   When?

Rachel   Just a few days ago. She was in the lane, making for her mother's cottage.

Sarah   Walking, was she?

Rachel   Walking – and it looked like she'd been walking a fair way.

Sarah   And she was alone?

Rachel   Alone, with her head down and her hood over her face, but I knew it was her, because she looked up when I spoke her name.

> *There is a flashback to this meeting. **Tess** enters, wearing a cloak, her face hidden by the hood. She walks with her head down. **Rachel** turns to her.*

Rachel   Tess. Tess – is it you?

> *Tess stops. She pulls back her hood.*

Tess   Rachel…

Rachel   It is you. Tess Durbeyfield – but it's not Durbeyfield anymore, is it?

Tess   What do you mean?

Rachel	We heard you were married.
Tess	Oh… yes… yes, I am married… five days ago.
Rachel	Still not used to it, I suppose. They say he's a gentleman, your husband.
Tess	He's a parson's son.
Rachel	He's not with you, though?
Tess	No… I've just come to see my mother… I shan't be staying long.
Rachel	Not now you've got somebody to hurry back to.
Tess	That's right.
Rachel	Well. I'll let you get on, then.

Tess turns, and moves away.

Rachel	It's wonderful how things can sometimes fall out.

Tess looks back to Rachel.

Rachel	When you think how things were for you, and how they are now. You must count yourself well-favoured.

> *Tess stares at Rachel, then pulls her hood over face and moves off, to stand apart. Rachel turns back to Sarah and continues the telling of her story.*

Rachel	Such a look she gave me. It went right through me, if you know what I mean. Right through me, like a blade of ice.
Sarah	It's true what we heard, then. She is married.
Rachel	So it seems.
Sarah	And it seems to me we haven't heard the half of it.
Rachel	What do you mean?

Sarah	If she is married, and to such a gentleman, what was she doing here alone, and walking? Why wasn't this gentleman of hers with her, and where is he?

*Joan enters to Tess for another flashback scene – the meeting between Tess and her mother in the Durbeyfield home. **Rachel** and **Sarah** freeze. **Tess** pushes back her hood.*

Joan	Gone away?
Tess	For a time.
Joan	Married on Tuesday and now it's Saturday and he's gone away!
Tess	Yes.
Joan	What for?
Tess	On business.
Joan	Business? What kind of business? What kind of husband is it that leaves his wife after five days of marriage, that's what I'd like to know.
Tess	He's a good husband, Mother – a good man.
Joan	Is he? Your looks and your voice don't seem to say so. There's more to this than you're letting on, Tess. Out with it, now, before your father comes back. *(She pauses)* You'll tell me sooner or later, so you might as well make it sooner.

There is another pause.

Tess	I told him.
Joan	What?
Tess	*(Raising her voice, and speaking more firmly)* I told him about what happened.
Joan	You fool! You little fool! After what I wrote to you? Why? Whatever possessed you?

Tess	I wanted to do right by him.
Joan	Do right by him? You should've thought of that before you married him.
Tess	I know. It was wrong of me. I should never have. But I wanted him so much. And I thought… I thought he might forgive me.
Joan	But he didn't.
Tess	No.
Joan	And now you've parted.
Tess	Yes.
Joan	For good?
Tess	I don't know.
Joan	Where is he?
Tess	Gone to look for a farm – he's given me some money.
Joan	Has he, now?
Tess	And there's more if I need it. And he said he'd write. He's a good man, Mother, and I've wronged him, and you and I must suffer for it.

John, Abraham and *Liza-Lu* enter. *They cry out in excitement and happiness.*

Liza-Lu	Look! It's Tess!
Abraham	Tess is come home!
John	Here she is! My girl! The gentleman's wife!
Liza-Lu	Is he here, Tess?
Tess	No.

Tess moves to stand a little way from her family, her head bowed and turned away from the audience.

John	A gentleman's wife, and a gentleman's daughter. Didn't I say it? Didn't I say everything would come out right for her in the end? It's in her blood, you see.
Joan	John –
Abraham	Did you come in a carriage?
Liza-Lu	When are we going to see him?
Abraham	Have you come to stay? Liza-Lu's got your bed, now.
John	Where is he, then? Let's see this husband of yours. I want to have a word with him about something.
Joan	He's not here.
John	I've been thinking, you see. About your name. I mean, he might be a parson's son, and that's all well and good, but does he know the noble family he's married into? It'd be just like you not to have told him –
Joan	John –
John	And it seems to me it might be better if he were to take your name, instead of you his. D'Urberville, I mean. His name's too ordinary for you. I'm fixed on it. You'll both take the name of d'Urberville –
Joan	In heaven's name, John, will you stop your rattling and listen!

There is a pause.

Joan	Liza-Lu. There's some washing in the tub outside needs wringing.
Liza-Lu	Mother –
Joan	Go and do it. And you, Abraham, give her a hand.

Abraham	But –
Joan	Go on! Both of you!

Liza-Lu and *Abraham* go. *Joan* turns to *John*.

Joan	Now, John. There's something I have to tell you.

They freeze, as we switch back to Rachel and Sarah again.

Sarah	And she's gone again, you say?
Rachel	That's right.
Sarah	And nobody knows where?
Rachel	No. To join her husband, maybe.
Sarah	Maybe. And maybe not. To my mind, there's something more to all this, and one day we'll find out the truth of it.

Sarah goes. Rachel speaks to the audience as she does. Tess turns back to her family and the audience.

Rachel	But we never did. And that was the last time I ever saw her. And when I next came across her name, it was to read it in the papers, which were full of the terrible thing she'd done.

Rachel goes. John looks at Tess, shakes his head sadly and walks off. Joan gives Tess a hard look and follows him. Tess is left alone. The Chorus enter, on their lines, to take up positions on and around one of the raised areas. They narrate Tess's journey from Marlott to the south.

Chorus 1	She travels south and west –
Chorus 2	By strange roads, unfamiliar landscapes –
Chorus 3	Shunning the places where people might know her –

Chorus 4   As winter becomes spring, spring becomes summer –

Chorus 5   Working in the dairies around Port Bredy.

Tess   And I thought nothing and felt nothing. I gave my body up to the work. As if part of me, the best part, had been cut out, and all that was left was a hollow space, an emptiness at the centre, a numb ache.

Chorus 6   Until the milk season ends and the weather cools –

Chorus 7   And she leaves the dairies to work the land –

Chorus 8   Stooping amongst the threshed wheat –

Chorus 9   And the cut stubble of the harvest fields.

Tess   Only sometimes, as I was working, my mind would go back to that summer before, and I'd think of him, and see him as I saw him then, and wonder where he was, and what had become of him. I thought he might write to me, and tell me where he was. But if he did, I never received the letter, so I didn't know.

> *Tess moves to sit on the raised area among the Chorus. Downstage, **Marian** enters and speaks to the audience.*

Marian   I knew. Izz was the one who found out. Not long after they were married, we both left Talbothays. The work there was finished for the season, and the heart had gone out of the place for us. I came here to work at Flintcomb-Ash farm, near Chalk Newton, and not long after I'd arrived, Izz came to see me, and told me she'd seen him. She'd gone to see them, she said, to tell them what had happened to poor Retty. But Tess wasn't there. There was only Angel, and he was alone.

> *There is a flashback scene to Izz's meeting with Angel. He enters, carrying the travelling bag, which he puts down. He looks around. **Izz** enters from the other side of the stage, and approaches Angel. He doesn't see her until she speaks to him.*

Izz   Sir? Mr Clare...

Angel turns.

Angel	Izz. Izz Huett. What are you doing here?
Izz	I came to see you – and Tess.
Angel	Tess isn't here – we aren't living here, now. I've just come back to collect a few things.
Izz	I hope she's well.
Angel	*(After a pause)* She is.
Izz	And you, sir? Are you well?
Angel	Yes, yes I am, Izz. I'm well enough.
Izz	*(Pointing to the travelling bag)* You're going away?
Angel	Yes. Far away. I'm leaving the country. I'm going to South America.
Izz	*(Shocked and upset)* South America… why?
Angel	They're offering land out there on good terms. I'm going to… investigate the prospects.
Izz	When will you be leaving?
Angel	In a few days' time. After I've said goodbye to my parents.
Izz	And… is Tess going as well?
Angel	No. She's gone back home to Marlott. I'll be going out there alone.

> *Reverend and Mrs Clare enter on another part of the stage, for a flashback scene with Angel. Angel turns to them and approaches them as they speak. Izz freezes.*

Rev. Clare	And shall we see your new wife before you go?
Angel	No.

Mrs Clare	I must say, Angel, I find this… rather odd.
Angel	What?
Mrs Clare	That you should be parting from her so soon – and that you don't even bring her here to meet us. Is there something wrong between you?
Angel	Wrong? No… of course not… what would there be?
Rev. Clare	We don't know, Angel. But after such a hasty marriage –
Angel	To tell you the truth – I wanted to… delay your meeting with her until… she was a little more refined and could be a credit to you.
Mrs Clare	A credit to us?
Angel	Yes.
Mrs Clare	You say she is honest, and hard-working?
Angel	Yes.
Mrs Clare	And virtuous?
Angel	Yes!
Rev. Clare	In short, Angel, she is a woman whose history would bear investigation?
Angel	Of course!
Mrs Clare	Then, I'm sure, Angel, that she is refined enough for us.

> *Reverend and **Mrs Clare** go. **Angel** looks across to where **Tess** is sitting among the Chorus. He speaks to the audience.*

| Angel | If I'd been what I should have been – what I wanted to be – I'd have gone back to her, begged her forgiveness for treating her so harshly. But I couldn't. I couldn't endure what she'd told me. So I left her and I left England and I went to South America. |

Angel picks up the travelling bag and goes. Izz watches him then turns and speaks to Marian.

Izz   And then he told me that they'd parted.

Marian   Parted? But why?

Izz   I don't know. They'd had some difference, he said, and had decided to part.

Marian   What difference could it be that's come between them?

Izz   It must have been something great… because he asked me to go with him, to South America.

Marian   He asked you? I don't believe it.

Izz   It's true, he did! And I almost said yes, but then I thought of Tess, and how nobody could love him more than her. So I refused and walked away from him, and I wish he'd never asked me, because now I don't think I'll ever be happy again.

*Izz goes. **Marian** turns and speaks to the audience.*

Marian   I thought of what Izz had told me, and I thought of Tess, and how happy she'd been when I last saw her, and of her sorrow now. So I wrote to her at her home in Marlott, thinking she might be in want of work and friendship. That was in the spring, but she didn't come here until the following winter.

*Marian moves to one side of the stage. Members of the **Chorus** make their way from the first raised area to the second, as they narrate Tess's further journeyings.*

Chorus 1   Travelling north and east through the broad uplands –

Chorus 2   Face pressed against the driving wind –

Chorus 3   Sky dark and heavy above her –

Chorus 4   Earth massive and heavy beneath her –

Chorus 5	A ragged outcast wandering the world's back.

Tess stands and speaks to the audience.

Tess	With the end of the harvest season, and no work to be had, I'd been forced to live on the money he'd given me, and all that was gone, now. He'd said if I was in need I could go to his father, but I wouldn't do that. I didn't want him to see me as I was now. I didn't want to bring shame on his son. And I was thinking how I could get through the winter, when Marian's letter finally reached me. So I set off at sunrise to walk to Chalk Newton, but the way was long and night found me still on the road.

*Tess moves wearily across to the second raised area as the **Chorus** continue their narration.*

Chorus 6	So she enters the wood at the road's side –
Chorus 7	Looks for a place of shelter and refuge –
Chorus 8	Crawls among the tangle of branches and brambles –
Chorus 9	Sleeps there, curled among the year's old leaves.

Tess lies curled on the raised area. The lights dim to a single light on her, which also dims so that she can just be seen.

. . . .

Scene 2

*The single light on **Tess** rises. She wakes, sits up, and speaks to the audience.*

Tess	I woke early, to the grey, hard light of a cold morning, and in the leaves beside me, I found a dead bird. It had frozen in the cold and its feathers were stiff. And it was so light when I held it in my hands, so light and delicate.

Tess	I buried it among the leaves, then left the wood and went on along the road, and by mid-morning the wind was up and the rain was falling, and I came at last to Flintcomb-Ash farm.

*The lights rise. **Tess** gets up, and moves to stand near **Marian**, as they both speak to the audience.*

Marian	And we worked there together in the open fields, cutting swedes out of the iron-hard earth –
Tess	Sunrise to sunset, in all weathers –
Marian	Frozen by the winter wind, faces raw and fingers bleeding –
Tess	Soaked to the skin in the icy rain.
Marian	Hard labour, and for little enough pay. I didn't think she'd bear it, but she did. There was a hardness in her eyes that hadn't been there before, and I wondered at the change that had come over her, but she never spoke of it, or anything that was past.
Tess	Not until one night in the barn after supper, when I spoke of the old, happy times at the dairy, and asked after the others.
Marian	And I told her then that Retty was dead.

Tess turns to Marian.

Tess	Dead? Retty? How… how did she die?
Marian	She was drowned. Last January it was, just a few days after you were married.
Tess	I didn't know… no one told me.

*Retty's spirit enters onto one of the raised areas. **Tess** and **Marian** freeze as **Retty** speaks to the audience, describing her own death.*

Retty	It was night and I went down to the river. The water was swollen by the winter floods, and I could hear it, roaring in the darkness, like some wild, hungry animal. It drew me towards it. I stepped forward, and I felt the water cold around my feet. I moved forward again, and it rose around my legs. I could feel its coldness in my body, its weight pulling at me. I knew now it would never let me go, so I just went forward, into the noise and the dark, and there was the coldness flowing over and through me, and the dark of the river filling my soul.

*Retty's spirit goes as **Marian** and **Tess** speak.*

Marian	I saw how she was – after the wedding – when the two of you drove away, so happy. I heard her weeping that night and the nights that came after. And when they pulled her from the river one morning, I knew there was only one cause of it.
Tess	Because I married him. Because he chose me as his wife. Poor Retty. To die for that. If only she'd known. If only she could see me as I am now!
Marian	Is it true, then? You have... parted?
Tess	Yes. It's true.
Marian	And have you parted forever?
Tess	At first I told myself not. That I'd wait for him and he'd return. But now... now I believe he will not. It was a senseless marriage we made, and a senseless death Retty died. And I'm to blame for it.
Marian	No, Tess. Not you.
Tess	Nor Angel. There's no blame in him.
Marian	No. If there's fault to be found, it's not in you or him.
Tess	Where, then? Where is the fault?
Marian	I don't know. In the world itself, perhaps.

*Marian turns from Tess, and leaves the
stage. Tess speaks to the audience.*

Tess   And it wasn't long after, that I received a letter from my
mother, telling me that Father had died. His heart had never
been strong, and it had finally given out on him. They were
leaving Marlott, she wrote, and coming to live at Kingsbere,
to be nearer to me. Kingsbere. A fitting place. The grave of
the d'Urbervilles.

Tess moves forward, to front centre stage.

Tess   I went out to the hilltop, where two roads meet. There was an
old stone there, worn by the weather. They said that the stone
marked the place where, in old times, a gallows had stood. The
day was dark and chill, and I stood there alone, and thought of
those who had been hanged there, and of Retty drowned in the
river, and I thought of Father, and all his dreams, and of the
bones of all those ancestors in their cold tombs – and I thought
too of the dead bird I'd found in the wood.

The Chorus step down from the raised area.

Chorus 1   And of all the poor creatures that live in the world –

Chorus 2   Whose suffering and sadness makes up the life of the world –

Chorus 3   That live and die in the world, without cause or reason –

Chorus 4   And the hills and the trees –

Chorus 5   The grasses and the stones –

Chorus 6   The rivers and streams, do they suffer too?

Chorus 7   Is the wind the voice of the world weeping?

Chorus 8   Call no man or woman happy in the world –

Chorus 9   Until their life's over and their suffering's done.

Tess   And I knew I'd never be at peace again, until I was as they
were now.

Tess sits. Alec enters unseen by Tess. He is dressed entirely in black, and carries a Bible and a crucifix. He speaks to the audience.

Alec   And that's where I saw her again, out at the crossroads by the gallows-stone, where I came to preach the salvation of the soul.

*Alec climbs up on a raised area as the **Chorus** gather around him to hear him speak.*

Chorus 1   The travelling preacher –

Chorus 2   The roadside sermonizer –

Chorus 3   Standing at the crossroads on a Sunday afternoon –

Chorus 4   With his Bible and his cross and his jet-black suit –

Chorus 5   Speaking to those who gather to hear him –

Chorus 6   A ranter –

Chorus 7   A raver –

Chorus 8   A real holy-roller –

Chorus 9   An excellent, fiery Christian man!

*Alec preaches to the Chorus. At the sound of his voice, **Tess** turns to look at him, rises, and walks slowly towards him in disbelief.*

Alec	Oh! My brothers and my sisters! Who among us is without sin? No one! Not one of us born to mortal flesh. We are all sinners, all doomed to die, and to stand in judgement before the wrath and vengeance of the Lord! And I too have been a sinner! I have sinned and led others into sin. But the word of God brought me to the light of truth. For even he that feels himself most damned is not beyond redemption. Even in the darkest hours of our suffering, we are not beyond the healing power of Christ's holy love! And what is it that Christ asks of us? Only that we should open our hearts to Him, and He will take our suffering from us, and lead us on the road to everlasting joy!

Tess stands beneath the raised area. She cries out. Her cry is both one of rejection of Alec's words, and horror at seeing who it is who speaks these words.

Tess	No. No! I won't believe it!

The Chorus stare at her in silence, then turn and go. Alec turns to look at her, and suddenly recognizes her.

Alec	*(Surprised)* Tess!

At the sound of his voice, Tess turns to make her way off, quickly, but he calls her back, sharply.

Alec	Tess! Wait!

The note of command in Alec's voice stops Tess against her will. He comes down from the raised area, and approaches her.

Alec	It's me – Alec.
Tess	Yes. I see it is.
Alec	Is that all you have to say to me?
Tess	What else is there to say?

Alec	That you're… happy to see me.
Tess	But I'm not.
Alec	Surprised, then, at least.
Tess	I'd rather I hadn't seen you at all.

Tess turns to go.

Alec	Don't go, Tess.

Alec steps round, blocking her path.

Tess	Let me go.
Alec	Not yet.
Tess	What is it you want with me?
Alec	I want… your forgiveness.

Tess and Alec freeze, as Marian enters, to one side of the stage, and speaks to the audience.

Marian	I didn't know who he was, or what he'd been to her. Only that he wouldn't leave her alone, that almost every day he'd be there, waiting for her. And that she'd go to him, as if there was, or had been, something between them.
Tess	Ask God for forgiveness, not me.
Alec	And I want… to make amends.
Tess	Make amends?
Alec	You've seen me preach. You've heard my words.
Tess	You're a fine one with words.
Alec	I'm not who I was. I'm a changed man.
Tess	No. You'll always be what you were.

Alec	I know I did you great wrong. And I want to make amends for it.
Tess	Nothing you could ever do would make amends for the hurt and the harm you've done to me!

Tess turns from Alec. They freeze again as Liza-Lu enters on another part of the stage and speaks to the audience.

Liza-Lu	Not long after we'd gone to live at Kingsbere, Tess came to see us, and Mother knew straight away there was something on her mind. Tess didn't want to tell her at first, but Mother wouldn't let her go till she'd found out what was troubling her. So, at last Tess did tell her. Mr d'Urberville had found her out, and was courting her again.
Alec	I can. I can make amends. I can make you my wife. It's the only way. To put right the wrong we did –
Tess	The wrong we did?
Alec	I know the fault was more mine than yours.
Tess	There was no fault in me at all.
Alec	Wasn't there? Are you so sure?
Tess	How can you say that?
Alec	Heaven led me here to you, Tess. Heaven means us to be together.
Tess	I can't be your wife. Even if I wanted to.
Alec	Why not?
Tess	Because I'm already married. And to a better man than you could ever be.

Tess and Alec freeze, as Marian speaks to the audience again.

Marian	As the days passed it troubled me to see her, with that shadow on her face, and the darkness in her eyes. For though I knew she feared him, it was as if she was drawn to him against her will, as if somehow he were drawing the life out of her.
Alec	Let me see him, then. I want to meet him. Where is this husband of yours?

*Tess tries to leave. **Alec** stops her.*

Tess	Please let me go.
Alec	I'd like to speak with him.
Tess	You can't.
Alec	Where is he? Here?
Tess	No.
Alec	Not here? Where, then?
Tess	Leave me alone.
Alec	He's not with you? What kind of husband is it leaves his wife alone, and in a place like this?
Tess	He's a good man.
Alec	And you don't even wear his ring.
Tess	It's here, around my neck.
Alec	Why don't you wear his ring?
Tess	It's no business of yours.
Alec	He's left you? Is that it? That's right, isn't it? He's left you!
Tess	Only for a little while.
Alec	Why? Why has he left you? Because of me? Because he found out about me?

Tess	Yes! Yes, he found out. I told him!
Alec	And you thought he'd forgive you. But he didn't. You were a fool to think he would.
Tess	He'll come back to me.
Alec	You think so? No. You don't. He won't come back to you, Tess, and you know it. You're alone in the world, and there's no one you can turn to but me. Because you were mine from the first –
Tess	No!
Alec	– and you'll be mine at the last.

Tess and *Alec* freeze, as *Joan* enters, near to Liza-Lu, and speaks to the audience.

Joan	And I said to her, it must be the way of things, and there's no going against it. Fate's brought him back to you, and by all accounts he's a changed man – and still a rich one. With your father gone, we have no means of livelihood but yours. Doesn't d'Urberville buy clothes for the children, I said? Doesn't he put good food on our table? Doesn't he help to keep this very roof over our heads? Think on your circumstances, and on ours, I told her. Think deep on it, Tess. He's come back to you and the other hasn't, and you bore his child, and in the eyes of heaven he's your natural husband.

Joan and *Liza-Lu* go. *Alec* turns to Tess.

Alec	You agree then?

Tess hesitates, then gives in.

Tess	Yes.
Alec	We'll leave here tomorrow. Find a more… suitable dwelling-place. No one will know us. We'll be as if man and wife. Mr and Mrs d'Urberville.
Tess	*(Flat and resigned)* Whatever you wish.

Alec	It's for the best. You'll come to see that. And with time, too, you'll come to be happy.
Tess	I've agreed to do what you say, Alec. Isn't that enough? And perhaps there is some justice in it. Perhaps we were meant to be together. If we were, then there's nothing else to be done. But don't expect me to be happy.
Marian	*(To the audience)* And then one day they were gone, the two of them, without a word and I didn't know where, and I was fearful for her, because when I thought of her it seemed to me that she was walking hand in hand with death.

> *Alec holds out his hand to Tess.* **Tess** *pauses then takes it. They exit.* **Marian** *watches them go and then exits too.*

· ·

Scene 3

> *Angel enters and speaks to the audience.*

Angel	In the early spring I came back to England to find her. Out there, thousands of miles away, weakened by fever, my whole venture in ruins, I'd finally come to realize that my new life was no life at all. I saw the pettiness and narrowness of my own soul, the gentleness and greatness of hers. I knew what it was I'd cast aside – the thing most precious to me, and nothing mattered to me now but to try and… win her back. So I set out in search of her. I tried Marlott, but she and her family had gone from there and no one could or would tell me where. She seemed to have vanished, disappeared from the face of the earth. Even so, I wouldn't give up. I couldn't. And, at last, I did have word of her, and traced her whereabouts to the farm at Chalk Newton.

> *Marian enters, and Angel turns to her. She speaks to him, cool at first, then growing in emotion.*

Marian	She was here, but not any more. She's gone.

Angel	How long?
Marian	Almost three months.
Angel	And you've no idea where?
Marian	No. *(Accusingly)* You should have come for her sooner.
Angel	I've been looking for her, ever since I came back to England.
Marian	You should never have left her.
Angel	I know.
Marian	She waited for you. She told herself you'd come back. But it was so long. And in the end, she gave up.
Angel	I've done her great wrong. But I'll put it right, when I find her.
Marian	If you find her.
Angel	I will! Isn't there anything else you can tell me?
Marian	There's a lot I could tell you! But as to where she is now, you could ask her mother. She might know. She lives not far from here, now, at Kingsbere.

> *Angel goes to thank her, but **Marian** turns quickly and exits. **Joan** and **Liza-Lu** enter. **Angel** approaches them eagerly.*

Joan	*(Coldly)* You came back at last, then. To find her, I suppose.
Angel	I tried at Marlott first, then found out you'd moved here.
Joan	Where my husband's ancestors rest their bones. God rest his soul, and rot theirs. He was a fool. But not so big a fool as you.
Angel	Has she written to you?
Joan	Yes.
Angel	Do you know where she's living?

Joan	*(Evasively)* I… I'm not sure…
Angel	Where did she write from?
Joan	Port Bredy – but I think she's moved from there now.
Angel	Where to?
Joan	I don't know. And even if I did –
Liza-Lu	*(Interrupting)* Sandbourne.
Joan	Liza –
Liza-Lu	*(Continuing quickly)* That's where you'll find her. At Sandbourne.
Angel	Thank you.
Joan	But perhaps it's best if you don't go there.
Angel	Why?
Joan	She's had enough trouble in her life. Let her alone, now. Leave her be.
Angel	I must go to her.
Joan	*(Forcefully)* I don't think she'd want you to!
Liza-Lu	*(To Joan)* No. I think she would. *(Turning to Angel)* I think if she knew you were here, and were looking for her, she'd want for you to go to her. She'd want it more than anything in the world.
Joan	What are you saying, girl?
Liza-Lu	The truth, Mother. And he knows it.
Joan	Well, perhaps you're both right. Maybe you know her better than I do. For though she's my own daughter, I don't think I've ever known her at all.

Joan goes. Liza-Lu gives Angel a smile of
encouragement, then follows her mother.
Chorus 1 – 8 enter on their lines, taking up
positions, in pairs, around the stage.

Chorus 1   He takes the coach south to Sandbourne, travels all through the day –

Chorus 2   Arrives at night in the seaside town and begins his quest –

Chorus 3   Walking the quiet streets, from door to door, each time asking the same question –

Angel   *(To Chorus 5)* Is there a woman staying here by the name of Durbeyfield?

Chorus 4   Each time receiving the same answer –

Chorus 5   I'm sorry, sir. There's no one of that name here.

Chorus 6   But he doesn't give up, he goes on with his search, on and on as the night deepens –

Chorus 7   Always asking that same question –

Angel   *(To the world in general)* Is there a woman staying here by the name of Durbeyfield?

Chorus 8   Until, at last, he receives the answer –

The landlady enters to Angel.

Landlady   Durbeyfield, sir? No, not Durbeyfield. But perhaps you're mistaken. Perhaps you mean d'Urberville. There is a woman staying here by that name.

Angel   Miss d'Urberville, yes –

Landlady   No, sir. Not Miss. Mrs. Mrs d'Urberville.

Tess enters wearing a white dress. She stares
at Angel in disbelief. The landlady stands to
one side.

Tess	Angel? *(She approaches him)* Is it you?
Angel	Yes… I've found you at last.
Tess	Found me?
Angel	I've been looking for you. *(He makes a movement towards her, she flinches back)* Can you forgive me, Tess? Can you take me back?
Tess	Take you back?
Angel	I want to make amends.
Tess	You as well!
Angel	What do you mean?
Tess	Why didn't you come sooner? Why did you wait till now?
Angel	I'm sorry. I should have done.
Tess	But you didn't.
Angel	No. I didn't realize –
Tess	I waited and waited for you, but you didn't come. And I was so worn and weary, and it was all so hard, and I gave up hope, and he said you wouldn't come, he kept on saying you'd never come again and I believed him.
Angel	I don't understand…
Tess	And now it's too late.
Angel	No!
Tess	It is. It's too late. I've gone back to him.
Angel	Gone back?
Tess	He's here with me, now.

Alec enters on the other side of the stage, unseen by *Tess* and *Angel*.

Tess	He's won me back.

*The **landlady** steps forward.*

Landlady	*(To Angel)* Will that be all, sir? Are you finished? I'm waiting to lock up, you see.
Angel	Yes. That's all. Thank you. I'm quite finished.

***Angel** turns and walks off. **Tess** stares with longing and despair after him. **Alec** watches Tess with wry amusement. The **landlady** turns and speaks to the audience.*

Landlady	They seemed a very respectable couple. He was a religious man, and she had all the bearings of a lady. I had no cause for complaint against them, not until that night when the other gentleman called, and after he'd gone, I heard… raised voices.

*The **landlady** moves to one side and watches the action. **Alec** steps up to Tess.*

Alec	So he did come back? I must say, it's something of a surprise. He must have been rather keen on you after all.

***Tess** turns on him, snapping in fury.*

Tess	He's my husband!
Alec	No, Tess. I am your true husband, in the eyes of God.
Tess	What has God to do with this! What has God to do with me!
Alec	What's this? Anger? Fury? And from my docile little Tess?
Tess	He should have danced with me that time.
Alec	What?
Tess	If he'd have danced with me, things would have been different. I think I knew it even then.
Alec	What is all this?

Tess	If we'd danced together then I would never have had to lay eyes on you! Never have been... touched by you.
Alec	You hate my touch, do you, Tess?

Alec strokes Tess's face with his fingers. She recoils from him.

Tess	Yes! I hate you, and everything about you!
Alec	Yet you came away with me. And you can't deny I've treated you well. And I see that your family doesn't go without. That's true, isn't it?
Tess	Yes...
Alec	And you wear the expensive clothes I've bought you? And you're content to live with me as my wife?
Tess	Yes! But only because –
Alec	What? Because what, Tess? Because part of you likes it? Because you can't help yourself?

Tess cries out at him in desperation.

Tess	Let me go to him! He's the better part of me... with him I am ... truly myself... only with him... you'll never have joy from me, you know that... you'll never have anything but... *this!* Please, Alec. I beg you, for both our sakes, let me go to him.
Alec	Is that what you want?
Tess	You know it is. Yes!
Alec	*(Mockingly)* Ah, Tess, if only I could. But it's impossible.
Tess	You won't?
Alec	I can't. It would be... a blasphemy. In the eyes of heaven, you belong to me.

She stares at him, and becomes suddenly quiet.

Tess	Yours first and last.
Alec	Yes.

> *Alec takes Tess by the arms, kisses her softly on her forehead, then turns from her towards the audience. Tess keeps her eyes on him.*

Tess	And only death will part us.

> *Chorus 9 enters carrying a knife. Tess walks across, takes the knife, and turns back to face Alec. The landlady turns once more to the audience.*

Landlady	If I'd known what was going to happen, I'd have gone up to them. But I didn't know. How could I? I didn't discover it until the next morning, when I saw the door open, and looked inside – and then I saw him lying there, poor man, and I realized what she'd done, and wondered what kind of creature she could be.

> *Tess looks at the landlady. The landlady starts, fearfully, and goes. Tess moves in slowly on Alec. He remains throughout with his back to her.*

Tess	He was standing with his back to me, looking out of the window. There was a knife on the table. I'd been cutting bread with it earlier. It was still where I'd left it. I picked it up and went across to him. At any moment I expected him to turn round and take the knife from me and laugh that laugh of his. But he didn't. There was a full moon in the sky. Its light filled the room. And then I knew it was the moon that he was looking at, it was the full moon that held his gaze so long. And I knew that this moment alone was mine, that there would only ever be this one chance, so I took it, and raised the knife, and I struck.

> *Tess clasps the knife in both hands and raises it above Alec's head. She holds it there for a moment, then brings it down behind his back. He lowers his head.*

Chorus 9	And it was done.

*Alec raises his head, and walks off-stage.
Chorus 9 takes the knife from Tess and puts
it down on the set before joining other members
of the Chorus. Angel enters, sees Tess, and
stops. She turns and approaches him.*

Tess	It's done.
Angel	Tess?
Tess	I knew you'd still be here somewhere – I knew you wouldn't leave me again.
Angel	I couldn't – I've been walking the streets all night.
Tess	So have I – looking for you – we're free of him, Angel. He won't trouble us any more.
Angel	You've left him?
Tess	I didn't think I'd have the strength. But then I thought of you, and the wrong he'd done you, and the wrong he did to me all those years ago.
Angel	Won't he come after you?
Tess	That's what I feared. He'd never let me go. That's why I knew it must be done. There was no other way to be free of him.
Angel	What do you mean, Tess? What have you done?
Tess	I've killed him. There was a lot of blood. So much blood. I remembered our horse that was killed. That was how it began, and now it's ended. With blood and with blood. But it had to be. It was ordained from the beginning. Heaven directed my hand.

Angel speaks to the audience.

Angel	We stood on the road just outside the town. The sun hadn't long risen, and there was no one else about. I saw her face in the early morning light, I heard the clear tones of her voice. And although at first I could hardly believe it, I knew what she was telling me was true.

Angel turns back to Tess.

Tess	You'll stay with me, now, won't you, Angel? You won't leave me again?
Angel	No, Tess. I won't leave you again.

> *Angel holds out his hand to Tess. She takes it, and they walk together towards one of the raised areas. They sit down as the* **Chorus** *speak.*

Chorus 1	They leave the highway, travel north across the country –
Chorus 2	Keep to hidden lanes and old tracks, walking on through the day –
Chorus 3	A warm day in May of clear skies and soft winds, taking them towards evening to an old, empty house –
Chorus 4	Set far back among trees, where they rest for the night.
Tess	I wish we could stay here forever. This is how we should have been. The two of us together, no shadow between us. But nothing lasts. Spring comes, and summer, and in autumn the flowers die. But when winter's past they come again. Moments are all we have, and in those moments we can be happy. I'm happy now, and I don't fear what's to come.

> *Tess and Angel rise, and move to centre stage.*

Chorus 5	And going on the next day with the sun's second rising, like creatures cast out and fleeing through the world –
Chorus 6	To come at last, with the sun's second sinking, to a wide plain where great stones rise –
Chorus 7	A circle of dark stones thrusting up through the earth –
Chorus 8	Moon-washed, mist-lit, silent as eternity –
Chorus 9	The place of sacrifice, the place of death.

Tess	Stonehenge. It was a pagan temple in old times. What did they worship here?
Angel	The sun, I think.
Tess	The sun. It's setting now. But we'll see it rise in the morning. We'll rest here.
Angel	It's too open. If anyone's following us –
Tess	They'll find us wherever we go. I know they'll come for me soon, and I'm ready. Don't be sad for me, Angel. Remember me as I am now. Look after Mother, and Abraham. And Liza-Lu. Look after her. There's something of me lives in her – the best of me perhaps. I'll sleep now. Watch for me, Angel. Wake me when the sun rises.

> *Tess* lies down. *Angel* stands apart from her. The *Chorus* speak, gradually moving in to stand around Tess, some on the floor, some on the two raised areas.

Chorus 1	She sleeps. Night passes. Dawn comes –
Chorus 2	As out of the early morning mist –
Chorus 3	Out of the shadows and rags of the dark –

Chorus 4	Figures are approaching, figures without faces –
Chorus 5	As if the stones themselves were moving –
Chorus 6	Encircling her, closing her in, here, where her life's path has always been leading –
Chorus 7	Every step she's taken a movement towards it –
Chorus 8	And the earth, or whatever spirit moves through the earth –
Chorus 9	Has finally decided to give her up.

Tess wakes, rises, and stands, centre stage.

Angel	They took her, and she went willingly, and I didn't see her again until the trial –

Liza-Lu enters on the opposite side to Angel.

Liza-Lu	– where they charged her with murder in the first degree, and she never said a word in her defence.
Angel	Nor when they found her guilty, and the judge passed sentence.
Liza-Lu	And on a warm, July morning, in the courtyard of the prison, the black flag was raised, and she was hanged.

Tess speaks to the audience.

Tess	There are times when you can sense something beyond you, a kind of spirit, in the trees and the hills and the rivers. And this spirit, you know it's part of you as well, or you're part of it, and it never dies, and you'll never die, because it's the spirit that moves through all things, and makes them one.
Chorus 1	And out of the sky the morning sun –
Chorus 2	Touches her head, a crown of fire –
Chorus 3	And the story's over, and the drama's done.

The lights fade slowly to a single light on **Tess.** *Then this too fades slowly to blackout.*

Activities

About the Author

Thomas Hardy was born in Higher Bockhampton, Dorset, on 2 June 1840. His father was a stonemason with a love of music, particularly country dances, and his mother 'read every book she could lay hands on'. These pleasures remained important to Hardy throughout his life – influencing his work, and his writing in particular.

In 1856, when he was sixteen, Hardy began training to be an architect, but he continued to read, and to study Latin and Greek, in his spare time. In 1862 he moved to London to work with another architect, Arthur Blomfield. Here he began to write. He was quite successful and published a number of essays and stories in journals and periodicals. He also began to write poetry.

In 1870, Hardy met Emma Gifford who encouraged him to write more. Unable to find a publisher for his poetry, Hardy tried his hand at writing novels. *Under the Greenwood Tree* was published in 1872, followed by *A Pair of Blue Eyes* in 1873. The success of these novels led Hardy to give up his work as an architect and concentrate on his writing.

Portrait of Hardy by
Reginald-Grenville Eves

Hardy and Emma married in 1874, and Hardy now began to write in earnest. His next novel, *Far From the Madding Crowd*, was set in his native Dorset, which he renamed Wessex. This set a pattern, and many of his following novels were set in the villages and country towns of Wessex. He wrote about the countryside he knew and loved, and the people who lived and worked there. He also wrote about the social and political issues which interested him, weaving them into his stories and expressing his opinions through the words and actions of his characters.

Hardy and Emma continued to live in London and Hardy wrote five more novels there. Increasingly, the same themes appeared in his writing:
- folklore and superstition
- local customs, ballads and celebrations
- the relationship between people and nature – the land, the weather, the seasons – and how this affects their daily lives
- what happens to people who break the rules of society
- relationships between parents and children
- old families – their names, their ancestors, and their importance
- fate – who or what controls our lives
- death.

Many of these themes appear in his later novels, too, including **Tess of the D'Urbervilles**.

In 1883, Hardy and Emma moved to 'Max Gate' near Dorchester. Here, Hardy began to experiment further and to tackle greater and riskier issues in his writing, resulting in his three most famous novels: *The Mayor of Casterbridge* (1886), **Tess of the D'Urbervilles** (1891) and *Jude the Obscure* (1896).

These last two novels offended many people. **Tess** was strongly criticized because it was the story of an unmarried mother, published at a time when sex before marriage (for women) was not acceptable in real life or in books. Hardy was upset by this reaction to his work. He published one more novel, *The Well-Beloved*, in 1897 before turning away from fiction to concentrate on his poetry.

In 1912 Emma Hardy died, and two years later Hardy married his second wife, Florence Dugdale, who was also an author. In his later years, he wrote an autobiography which was published by his wife after his death in January 1928.

His novels are still widely read and studied today, and many of them have been filmed for the cinema and television.

About the Novel

Censorship of Victorian Literature

Read

In the late Nineteenth century, there was a strict moral code of behaviour laid down by the Victorian church and the government. However, many people broke the rules, even if they only did so in secret. Writers often wanted to write about people and society as they really were – not as they were supposed to be. But these writers found that they, too, were bound by rules:

- They were not allowed to write about sex.
- Woman characters had to be completely pure.
- Women characters of 'easy virtue' must eventually die (murder and suicide was acceptable) or be sent off to Australia as convicts!
- Babies born outside marriage should die at birth or soon afterwards.

'The Lost Path', by Frederick Walker. This nineteenth-century painting has two meanings: the woman with her baby has lost her way in the snow, but the title also suggests she has 'strayed from the path of virtue': she is a 'fallen woman' and her baby was born outside marriage.

'The Awakening Conscience', by William Holman Hunt. Again, this shows the Victorians' view of morality: the couple are not married. The young woman is starting to feel the pangs of guilt, but the symbols in the painting suggest it is already too late: she is a 'fallen woman'.

However, it was acceptable for men to have sex outside marriage. The Victorians were prepared to turn a blind eye to this!

In this climate, Thomas Hardy began to write **Tess of the D'Urbervilles** in 1888 for a newspaper syndicate, Tollotson and Son. But, having read part of the manuscript, the publishers objected to certain events in the story, arguing that they would offend their readers and the Victorian establishment. Hardy did not want to make any changes and so the contract was cancelled.

Hardy tried two further magazines, but they also turned down the story. Finally, he decided he would have to do something if he wanted to get it published. He made a number of cuts, including any references to the birth, death, and burial of Tess's illegitimate baby. He also introduced a new slant to the storyline: in his revised story, Alec tricks Tess into a false marriage; when she discovers his deception, she leaves him and returns home to her family.

Discuss   1   What, if anything, would be lost from the playscript (and the novel) if Tess's baby, Sorrow, did not exist?

2   Would our opinion of either Alec or Tess change if the false marriage story was included in this adaptation?

The story was then published in weekly instalments in the magazine, *The Graphic*, between 4 July and 26 December 1891.

Publication of the Novel

Read

When the story was published as a novel in November 1891, Hardy put back the material he had cut from the story. There was an immediate reaction from the reviewers.

A critic for *The Saturday Review* wrote: 'Mr Hardy, it must be concluded, tells an unpleasant story in a very unpleasant way...' while *The Independent* disliked this 'study of adultery'. A reviewer in *The Nation* described Tess as 'a weak and sensual woman', Alec as 'an incorrigible rogue', and Angel as 'the only moral character in the novel'.

Discuss

1   What do the descriptions given to Tess, Alec, and Angel by the critic writing in *The Nation* actually mean?
2   Do you agree with any of them?

Read

Other critics were up in arms about Hardy's sub-title to **Tess of the D'Urbervilles**: 'A Pure Woman'.

Discuss

1   Why were people upset by this description of Tess?
2   Why do you think Thomas Hardy called Tess 'a pure woman'?
3   Do you agree with him?

Alternative Title

An early title for Hardy's story of Tess was *Too Late, Beloved*.

Discuss

1   Why do you think that Hardy considered this an appropriate title?
2   Which of the two titles do you prefer and why?
3   Can you come up with any further titles which might be appropriate?

Write

Write down an idea for your own story or playscript with the title, *Too Late, Beloved*. You could go on to develop it into a full-length story or script.

What the Adapter Says

When I came to work on dramatising **Tess of the D'Urbervilles**, two things struck me immediately. One was the simplicity of the story that lies at the heart of the novel. The other was the important part played by the rural landscape and the changing seasons.

The story of Tess – a woman wronged and abandoned by her lover – is the sort of story you find in many folk-songs and ballads, the kind of songs Hardy himself would have been familiar with.

It is also a story which is firmly rooted in the landscape in which it takes place.

The landscape plays a very important part in the novel of **Tess of the D'Urbervilles**. To most of us today, 'the countryside' is a place we visit for days out, and 'the landscape' a pretty picture-postcard view of hills and trees. But the world in which Tess lives is almost entirely dependent on the land – bound up with the yearly cycle of birth, growth, decay and re-birth. For Tess and her people, their way of life is rooted in the life of the earth. It has been like this, more or less unaltered, for thousands of years. In pre-Christian times the earth was worshipped as the Great Goddess, the giver of life and death, and Tess's people still think of the earth as a living, all-powerful spirit which runs through every aspect of their lives.

The more I thought of it, the more I felt that Tess's story is also the story of that all-powerful landscape, and its yearly cycle of birth, growth and decay. Her tragic fate is the fate of the earth, the inevitable turning of the year from spring to winter, life to death.

In the novel, Hardy was able to describe the landscape and show how it dominates the lives of his characters. But in a play you cannot write long descriptive passages. A play must be immediate and dramatic; characters speak and act; they move through a series of events and actions, towards whatever end is in store for them. So when I began to write this play I had to find a different way of showing the audience how the forces of the landscape and the forces of fate dominate Tess's story.

Now, I knew that Hardy was particularly attracted to Ancient Greek tragedy, and that one of the most important 'characters' in Ancient Greek tragedy is the Chorus. In Greek plays, the Chorus is a group of actors who do more than just narrate the story: they act as a bridge between the audience and the characters onstage, to interpret events for us, comment on them, oversee the action almost like gods.

Ancient Greek tragedy also concentrates on the tragic fate of a single individual. It seemed to me perfectly right, then, to create the dramatisation of **Tess** along the lines of a Greek tragedy, with Tess as the tragic hero, and a Chorus as the voice of the landscape.

I also wanted, from the beginning, to place Tess onstage as the central character. She is the centre of the drama, and everything and everyone else revolves around her. That's why I decided to begin with Tess alone on stage. The song she's singing when we first see her – the ballad of a wronged woman – is significant too: it's as if she's singing her own story, almost. She's then joined by the Chorus, who will tell the story of her fate throughout the play.

In this way I hope I've succeeded in creating a piece of theatre which combines elements of folk-ballad and tragic drama, while giving the landscape of Wessex the same importance it has in Hardy's novel.

Working within this structure meant making changes to Hardy's original. But that was inevitable: the novel and the play are two entirely different forms, with different demands and needs. What I tried to do was to return to the essence of the novel – the simple, powerful story at its centre. I used the major events and characters of the story as a guide to my writing, but in the early stages of writing, I pretended there was no novel, only a sketch based on a ballad, and it was that sketch I worked from.

At a later stage, of course, I went back to the novel for a variety of reasons – to check details of dialogue, character and events – but mainly to make sure that the play remained true to the spirit of the original novel.

As it turns out, I think my play is a little less bleak and tragic than Hardy's novel. In the novel, Hardy hints at Tess's spirit living on in her sister, Liza-Lu. I wanted to go further than this. Because, on one level, Tess is the 'spirit' of the landscape, then her death cannot be the end, but only a new beginning, a renewal, a turning of the cycle from death to birth again. I've tried to suggest this is the case in the final moments of the play.

Lastly, a word about the language. Hardy has his rural characters speak in a West Country dialect. This firmly roots them in a particular part of the country, his part-real, part-imagined Wessex. But I felt that the play shouldn't be confined to one locality. The story has such a universal quality, I wanted it to be free to be set in whatever part of the country its performers and audience lived in. So, I've dispensed with the dialect, in the hope that others will provide their own.

David Calcutt

Tess Durbeyfield

Write and Discuss

1   Using only fifty words, write down the story of Tess Durbeyfield's life to include:
  - who she is
  - what happens to her.

2   Swap stories with a partner and discuss who has written the best description.

3   Each pair should read out their chosen description to the rest of the class.

4   As a class, decide which of the paragraphs best describes Tess's story. If you cannot pick out one which you prefer, you could combine sentences from several different paragraphs to make a new one.

Talk and Write

1   In small groups, brainstorm on a large sheet of paper all the words you would use to describe Tess – both her physical appearance and her personality.

2   Make a large spidergraph with Tess at the centre and add the words from your brainstorm to it. You may choose to set it out like the example below.

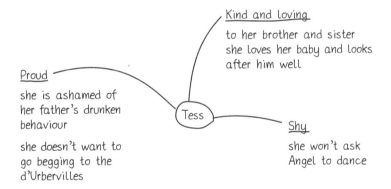

Kind and loving
to her brother and sister
she loves her baby and looks
after him well

Proud
she is ashamed of
her father's drunken
behaviour

she doesn't want to
go begging to the
d'Urbervilles

Tess

Shy
she won't ask
Angel to dance

3   Find evidence from the playscript to support your view of Tess. Add this to your diagram.

4   Finally, display the spidergraphs in your classroom.

Picture Research

1   You may also like to look through magazines and newspapers to find a picture of a girl who looks as you imagine Tess would look. She does not need to be wearing period clothes – her face and expression are the most important things.

2   Write a few lines on why this girl is Tess to you.

3   Display the photographs and your explanations for everyone in the class to see.

Discuss   1   If you were the producer working on a TV or film adaptation of
                     this playscript, which actress would you choose to play the part of Tess
                     and why?
               2   Form a small group to discuss the casting of your version of **Tess of the
                     D'Urbervilles**. Each 'producer' should put forward their choice and
                     explain why they want their chosen actress for the role.
               3   Vote to make a decision. If there are four candidates, write 1, 2, 3, 4 in
                     order of preference next to their names. Then add up the numbers.
                     The candidate with the lowest score is your choice to play Tess. If there
                     is a draw, you will have to make the hard decision of choosing between
                     the two.

Justine Waddell in the
title role of Tess in the
LWT 1998 TV version

Tess and Destiny

Read   Thomas Hardy used Tess's story to express his feelings about many
                issues: innocence and sacrifice; the strict moral code of Victorian society;
                the changing landscape of his beloved Wessex; the increased use of
                machinery on the land and how it threatened the old, traditional way
                of life. But one of the most important aspects of Tess's story is the
                role that fate and destiny play in it. He created Tess as a tragic figure,
                an innocent in a cruel world, swept helplessly along by the events of
                the story.

Discuss   In Act 1, Scene 1 a discovery is made that sets Tess's world on its head.
               1   What is this discovery and who makes it?
               2   What happens as a result?
               3   How does Tess feel about this?
               4   How does it change Tess's life?

Nastassia Kinski
in the title role of
Tess in the Roman
Polanski film of
the book

Read and List

Tess starts her life's journey down a path that seems to be mapped out
for her. There are lots of examples in the playscript that suggest that
Tess must stay on this path, that she cannot escape from it and that she
has no control over what happens to her.

1   Working in groups, look at the words spoken by both the Chorus and
    Tess herself throughout the playscript.

2   Make a list of everything they say that suggests that there is only
    one route for Tess to take leading eventually to her ultimate destiny.
    Start at Act 1, Scene 1 and set it out like this:

Act/Scene	Who says it?	What do they say?
Act 1, Scene 1	Chorus 6 Chorus 7 Chorus 8 Chorus 9	But there's only one story we can live – Only one tale our lives can tell – The one fixed into us at our very beginning – And we must live it through to its bitter end.

Discuss

1   Is Tess responsible for what happens to her?

2   Does she try to break away from the path? Can she choose her
    own destiny?

3   Find a moment in the play when you feel Tess could have acted
    differently to change things. How might the story have ended if she
    had been successful?

Blighted World

The more Tess sees of the world, the more she believes that she lives on a 'blighted star'.

Discuss   1   What do you think the phrase 'blighted star' means?
              2   Is there ever a time in the play when Tess is happy?

Write   1   What is the saddest part of the play for you and why?
              2   What is the happiest part of the play for you and why?
              3   Get into pairs or groups and compare your choices. Are they different or the same?

Tess's Baby

Read   Tess lived in late-Victorian England, when both society and the church had strict rules about behaviour and morality. It was considered wrong to have a baby without being married, and Tess could expect her neighbours in the village and the parson at her local church to disapprove of her situation.

Another scene from the Polanski film of **Tess**.

Discuss   Look back at Act 1, Scene 3 (pages 42-45).
              1   What do the villagers say about Tess and her baby?
              2   Do they feel disgust or sympathy for her situation?
              3   Why is Tess so keen to baptize her baby?
              4   Whose job is it to do this?
              5   What does Tess say to Abraham and Liza-Lu to reassure them that they must baptize the baby themselves?
              6   Why won't the parson bury the baby inside the churchyard?
              7   Is he right to refuse?

Write

1 Write an extra scene for the playscript in which Tess goes to the parson to ask him to bury Sorrow. You may find the questions you discussed on page 124 helpful in giving you ideas for this scene. You could make the parson an unsympathetic character – but in Hardy's original novel, the parson seems a kind man who would really like to help Tess. Experiment with the parson's character and decide which version you prefer.

2 Then write another scene in which Tess comes back home to tell her family the parson's decision. It may help you to re-read the end of Act 1, Scene 3, before you begin to write.

'The Outcast', by Richard Redgrave. Again, this gives us a view of Victorian morality: here, a father is ordering his daughter (on the right) from the house – presumably because her baby is illegitimate. Unmarried mothers were often disowned by their families; pregnancy outside marriage was a source of shame.

Tess the Goddess

Research

In the play, one of the characters compares Tess to a goddess.

1 Which character is this?
2 Who is the goddess? Find out some information about her.
3 Is this an appropriate description of Tess?
4 Why do you think she reacts angrily to the comparison?

Tess's Crime

Write

Rachel says of Tess in Act 3, Scene 2:
'...that was the last time I ever saw her. And when I next came across her name, it was to read it in the papers, which were full of the terrible thing she'd done.'

1 Tess has been convicted of Alec d'Urberville's murder and has been sentenced to death. Imagine that you have to write a report for a popular newspaper about Tess and her crime. You want some background information on her situation and personality. Who would you ask for
   - a sympathetic view of Tess
   - an unsympathetic view?

2 In two columns headed 'sympathetic' and 'unsympathetic', make lists of the characters you would like to interview.

3 Using evidence from the playscript, find examples of what each of these people thinks and/or says about Tess.

4 Using all or some of this information, write two news reports:
   - the first which presents a sympathetic view of Tess, her crime and her situation
   - the second which takes a more negative view, and accepts no excuses for her actions.

You should try to use quotations from the other characters in the play within your report, as in a real news story.

A Timeless Story

Villager 1   It's the old story.
Villager 2   We've heard it before, and we'll hear it again.

The story of Tess Durbeyfield is a timeless one. It is the subject of both old ballads and modern soap operas.

Research   1   What is a ballad? Find a definition of a ballad that you understand.
2   Research and read some ballads. You may also find recordings of ballads set to music. Try your local library. Folk music will give you lots of examples.

Read and Discuss   Read the ballads in this playscript. Which one do you like best?

Write   Write you own ballad based on Tess's story. You might prefer to choose a popular tune and set words to it.

Write   Plan a number of episodes for a modern soap opera – make one up or choose one of your favourites. Develop a storyline where a young girl is treated badly by her boyfriend and abandoned to her fate. Does her story end as Tess's does? Your modern version might have a different ending.

Alec d'Urberville

Read

Simon Stoke, Alec's father, made lots of money in the north of England. Once rich, he decided to move to the south and become a country gentleman. He built a large house in Trantridge and bought himself the name of an old extinct family – d'Urberville – and then died. Alec is his only son, and the heir to all his property and wealth.

Jason Flemyng as Alec d'Urberville in the LWT 1998 TV version of **Tess of the D'Urbervilles**

For the purpose of this activity, Alec's life can be divided into two parts:
- Act 1, Scene 2
- Act 3, Scenes 2 and 3

Write   1   Write a short paragraph about Alec and what he does during these phases of his life.

List   2   Make a list of the all the people who know Alec d'Urberville during each of these periods of his life. You could include characters like Alec's mother who does not appear in the playscript. Set the list out in two columns. Some people, like Tess, will appear in both columns.

Who Knows Alec?	
Act 1, Scene 2	Act 3, Scenes 2-3
Tess Car Darch	Tess

Role Play   3   Make a list of all the questions you would like to ask each person about
                  Alec and the way he lives his life. Here are some suggestions to get you
                  going:
                  • What was your first impression of Alec as a person?
                  • Is there anything about him that you do not like?
                  • How does he treat his workers? Is he a good employer?

             4   Choose members of the class to take the roles of the characters on
                  your list.

             5   Hot seat/interview the people listed in the first column about Alec and
                  his behaviour during this time. Then move onto the second group.

             6   Next, choose someone to take on the role of Alec and ask him about his
                  relationship with Tess – both before he seduces her and afterwards,
                  some years later, when he meets her for the second time. You could use
                  the questions below as a starting point:
                  • What was your first impression of Tess?
                  • Did you know why Tess suddenly left Trantridge and went back
                    home to Marlott? How did you react to this?
                  • What were your feelings when you saw her unexpectedly some years
                    later?
                  • Do you think you behaved badly towards her?
                  • Do you regret anything about your relationship with Tess?

Discuss   7   When you have finished, use the evidence you have heard to answer the
                  following questions:
                  • What sort of picture do you get of Alec d'Urberville?
                  • What are the bad things he has done?
                  • Has he done any good things?
                  • Does he change from his first appearance in Act 1 to his last in Act 3?
                  • Is his conversion to Christianity believable?
                  • Does he deserve to die?

Leigh Lawson as
Alec d'Urberville in
the Roman Polanski
film of the book

Angel Clare

Peter Firth as
Angel Clare in the
Roman Polanski
film of the book

Discuss

Thomas Hardy gave this character an unusual name. In the novel, he also plays a harp.

1   Why do you think that Hardy chose the name Angel?
2   Is it an appropriate name for him?

Write

1   Write a number of extracts from Angel's diary written during the time that he works at Talbothays, up to his wedding with Tess. Below is a list of some of the scenes you might include:
   - his decision not to enter the church but instead to become a farmer (Act 2, Scene 1)
   - the effect this has on his parents (Act 2, Scene 1)
   - his job at Talbothays and the people he works with (Act 2, Scenes 1 and 2)
   - his first meeting with Tess (Act 2, Scene 1)
   - their courtship (Act 2, Scene 2).
2   Then write Angel's diary entry for the night of Tess's confession. What are his innermost thoughts about Tess and his future?
3   Read a selection of the diary entries aloud to the class. In what way do Angel's feelings about Tess change?

Hot Seat

1   If you could choose just one question to ask Angel Clare about any part of his life, or anything he does, what would it be?
2   Collect all these questions and write them on the board or a large sheet of paper.
3   Then choose a member of the class to be Angel, put him in the hot seat and ask him some of these questions.
4   What do you think of his answers?

Alec and Angel

Debate

Using the information from the hot seating of Alec and Angel, the discussions which followed and any other evidence from the playscript, prepare a debate on the question:
Who does the most damage to Tess: Alec or Angel?

1   You will need two small groups: one to accuse Alec and one to accuse Angel. (The rest of the class will listen to what they say and then vote.)
2   Each group prepares their reasons why they think Alec/Angel did the most damage to Tess.
3   Choose a spokesperson from each group.
4   In turn, both sides put forward their arguments.
5   Allow time for audience questions and comments.
6   Then take a vote: who **did** do the most damage to Tess?

Oliver Milburn as Angel Clare in the LWT 1998 TV version of **Tess of the D'Urbervilles**

Telling Tess's Story

Read and Discuss

In the novel **Tess of the D'Urbervilles**, Hardy makes links between Tess's life and her environment. He uses long descriptive passages about the landscape, the weather, and particularly the passing seasons to emphasize both the good and the bad things that happen to Tess. In the playscript, David Calcutt uses the Chorus to provide this description.

1   Look at the lines spoken by the Chorus on pages 41 and 47. What are they describing?
2   What kind of mood does each description create – eerie, frightening, unhappy, or happy, carefree, optimistic?
3   What does each description tell us about that particular time in Tess's life?

Greek chorus from the National Theatre production of *The Oresteia*

Read and Discuss

The Chorus also gives the audience information about events which take place and how characters react to them. They summarize parts of the story and they act as narrators – telling us what is happening and why it is important.
Read what David Calcutt has written about his decision to use a Chorus in What the Adapter Says (pages 119–120).

1   Was this a good thing to do?
2   If he hadn't used a Chorus, what other techniques might David Calcutt have used to put across what they say to the audience?

List and Discuss

As well as the Chorus, other characters in the play act as narrators, speaking directly to the audience and telling them the story. Tess is one of them, but people who know her also act in this way.
Make a list of all the other characters, aside from Tess, who act as narrators. You will probably need to look back at the play before you do this.

Discuss and
Design

1   In what ways are the Chorus different from the other narrators as characters?
2   How might this difference affect what they wear on stage? Should they look similar or different from other characters in the play?
3   Design some costumes for the Chorus.

Jack Dollop and Rebecca Brooke's Story

Some people believe that Thomas Hardy wrote **Tess of the D'Urbervilles** as a classical tragedy. In this type of story or play, the hero or heroine struggles throughout against the destructive power of their own personality and other hostile forces outside themselves. Classical tragedies usually have their lighter, more comic moments to relieve the tension created by the dreadful things happening to the hero or heroine. Jack and Rebecca's story can be seen as such a moment.

Act

1   In groups of five, rehearse and perform Jack and Rebecca's story as a short play.

2   Make your characters over-the-top. Play it for laughs and see how it works.

3   Perform it to an audience and see their reaction.

Discuss

1   Do you think the story of Jack and Rebecca serves any purpose other than comic relief? Can you see any links with Tess's story?

2   Who did you feel most sorry for – Rebecca or Jack?

3   Compare Rebecca's mother, Mrs Brooke, with Tess's mother, Joan, and discuss the following points:
- How does each woman react to her daughter's betrayal?
- How do they deal with the men they believe to be responsible?
- Whose methods do you prefer?

4   What effect does the story have on Tess?

Retty's Death

Discuss

1   What effect does Retty's death have on Tess?

2   In the novel, Retty does not drown. Why do you think David Calcutt chooses to kill her in his adaptation?

Plays in this series include:

Across the Barricades   ISBN 0 19 831272 5
   Joan Lingard   adapted by David Ian Neville

The Bonny Pit Laddie   ISBN 0 19 831278 4
   Frederick Grice   adapted by David Spraggon Williams
                   with Frank Green

The Burston School Strike   ISBN 0 19 831274 1
   Roy Nevitt

The Canterbury Tales   ISBN 0 19 831293 8
   Geoffrey Chaucer   adapted by Martin Riley

Carrie's War   ISBN 0 19 831295 4
   Nina Bawden   adapted by Robert Staunton

The Demon Headmaster   ISBN 0 19 831270 9
   Gillian Cross   adapted by Adrian Flynn

Frankenstein   ISBN 0 19 831267 9
   Mary Shelley   adapted by Philip Pullman

Hot Cakes   ISBN 0 19 831273 3
   Adrian Flynn

Jane Eyre   ISBN 0 19 831296 2
   Charlotte Brontë   adapted by Steve Barlow and Steve Skidmore

Johnny and the Dead   ISBN 0 19 831294 6
   Terry Pratchett   adapted by Stephen Briggs

Paper Tigers   ISBN 0 19 831268 7
   Steve Barlow and Steve Skidmore

A Question of Courage   ISBN 0 19 831271 7
   Marjorie Darke   adapted by Bill Lucas and Brian Keaney

Smith   ISBN 0 19 831297 0
   Leon Garfield   adapted by Robert Staunton

A Tale of Two Cities   ISBN 0 19 831292 X
   Charles Dickens   adapted by Steve Barlow and Steve Skidmore

Tess of the D'Urbervilles   ISBN 0 19 831439 6
   Thomas Hardy   adapted by David Calcutt

The Turbulent Term of Tyke Tiler   ISBN 0 19 831269 5
   adapted from her own novel by Gene Kemp